Mills & Boon Best Seller Romance

A chance to read and collect some of the best-loved novels from Mills & Boon—the world's largest publisher of romantic fiction.

Every month, four titles by favourite Mills & Boon authors will be re-published in the *Best Seller Romance* series.

A list of other titles in the *Best Seller Romance* series can be found at the end of this book.

Robyn Donald

BRIDE AT WHANGATAPU

MILLS & BOON LIMITED
LONDON · TORONTO

First published 1977
Australian copyright 1984
Philippine copyright 1978
This edition 1984

ISBN 0 263 74614 3

Set in Linotype Plantin 10 on 10½ pt.
02–0384

Made and printed in Great Britain by
Richard Clay (The Chaucer Press) Ltd,
Bungay, Suffolk

CHAPTER ONE

FIONA WARD was nervous. It showed in the way her slender fingers clasped the top of her handbag so tightly that they showed white against the darkness of the leather. It showed in the tension of her dark grey eyes, the tight line of her mouth, usually so soft and generous. On her finger the narrow gold wedding ring stood out like a band of servitude oddly at variance with the extreme youthfulness of her features, for although she was twenty-three she looked no older than nineteen. Only her eyes, set in darkness, shadowy with the remembrance of old pain, revealed that she was no child fresh from school.

The waiting became unbearable. So much depended on this interview! Jonathan's health, her own peace of mind, all waited on the man who was behind that impersonal, mocking hotel door. The doctor had said that Jonathan must have at least a year in the country, to run wild in the fresh air if he was to get rid of that terrible cough which had racked his small body through the winter. Pray God that this interview would go well, that she would be able to leave cold, wet Wellington for that lovely northern peninsula of New Zealand where the sun lay hot and caressing over the warm land.

It had seemed like an answer to prayer when the efficient Mrs Dobbs at the employment agency had told her of the position.

'Secretarial,' she murmured, 'some knowledge of book-keeping desirable, but not absolutely necessary.'

Those wise brown eyes had been compassionate as they rested on the thin figure of the girl across the desk. Mrs Ward seemed so terribly young to be widowed, and yet she was the mother of a four-year-old son. It was tragic that her dead husband hadn't been able to leave her provided for, instead of forcing her into a hopeless search for a position where her child would be welcome.

'It sounds ideal for you, Mrs Ward. The property is very large, one of the original stations, I believe; and the house is an old Colonial residence. The owner needs some-one to help him with his paperwork. He would share you with his mother who is an author of some repute. That should keep you busy enough. The salary is good, and they have no objection to a child. Apparently one of the shep-herds' wives is prepared to look after him during working hours. It is a coastal property, with the house by the beach. Most of these old homesteads were built when Northland had few roads and the only easy access was by sea.'

'It ... it sounds ideal,' Fiona said quietly, seeing Jonathan brown and suntanned, healthy and carefree as he ran and shouted in the sunlight. With an effort she dragged her mind back to reality. Thank God her father had insisted on her taking a secretarial course after Jonathan was born.

Mrs Dobbs nodded. 'Here's the address. The owner is staying at the Settlers' Hotel. Your appointment is at four tomorrow. Just go in and ask to see Mr Smith.'

'Smith?'

Mrs Dobbs smiled. 'Yes. That's not his real name, of course, but don't worry, Mrs Ward. We've dealt with the family for years, and you will come to no harm with the ... Smiths. Good luck!'

Well, she needed some good luck just now. Jonathan ... but she refused to think of Jonathan. The sound of move-ment behind the door caused Fiona to press her trembling lips together and relax the tight knots that were her fingers. At all costs she must appear calm and confident! Mr Smith, whoever he was, must not realise how desperately she needed this job; she owed her pride that much.

He opened the door and walked through, saying in deep, deliberate tones, 'Mrs Ward? I'm sorry to keep you wait-ing ...' His voice tailed off as he saw her.

He was tall, dark, cruelly handsome, obviously wealthy,

full of that assurance which comes from complete self-confidence.

White-lipped, she whispered, 'No ... no!' holding her hands out as though to ward him off, then the room spun, and she felt herself sliding sideways across the wooden arm of the chair into a whirling, hideous oblivion.

Nausea gripped her, thickening her throat. With a shaking hand she pushed a strand of hair back from her clammy brow. For a moment she wondered what had happened, then a glass was pressed to her lips and Logan Sutherland said crisply, 'Drink this.'

A great shudder shook her too-slender form as recollection flooded back, and with it fear and despair.

'No,' she said, in hardly audible tones, then choked as fiery liquid was poured ruthlessly down her throat.

'It's only brandy. Will you drink it, or shall I tip the rest down your throat?'

Slowly Fiona opened her eyes. He was kneeling beside the sofa, an iron-hard arm across her shoulders, his expression cold but purposeful.

'I'll drink it,' she said shakily.

'Good.' He put the glass on the table, then stood up, looking down at her with eyes that were like chips of blue ice. 'Hurry up.'

The crystal rattled against her teeth as she sipped the liquor slowly, head downbent to avoid that accusing glance. Only when it was finished did he move away to stand with his back to her, staring out of the window.

Fiona swung her legs down on to the floor, trying with a spinning head to get her bearings. She was in a sitting-room, elegantly furnished, with vases of multicoloured freesias on the furniture. Their scent was pervasive, mockingly seductive, sweetly evocative. Feverishly she looked for her handbag, saw it on the table by the empty brandy glass and seized it. On the pretext of getting a comb out she took her son's photograph and carefully, with her eyes on the still figure by the window, stuffed it into her wallet, crushing it in the process. The crackling noise seemed to echo around the room, but she knew that this was only because of her tension. He could not possibly hear so soft a sound. Then she combed her copper tresses quickly, pushing the heavy weight of her hair back from her face, replaced the comb and snapped the bag shut.

'I . . . I feel better now,' she said.

'Good.' He turned and surveyed her keenly. 'Yes, there's some colour in your cheeks. Are you sure you're all right?'

'Yes, thank you.' She stood up, felt the room sway, and hurriedly put out a hand to the arm of the sofa. 'I'm fine,' she said determinedly. 'I'll go now.'

'Why?'

She stared at him in astonishment. 'Why?' she repeated like an idiot. 'I . . . I should think that that's obvious. You certainly don't want me to work for you, and I——' her voice became stronger, 'I don't want to work for you.'

'Possibly.' But he made no effort to open the door for her, which was unusual for one who possessed that instinctive courtesy she remembered so well. 'I don't think you should go yet, though. That was a long drink, and if I remember rightly you have no head for alcohol.'

Shamed colour flared in her cheeks, but she returned coldly, 'I'm all right, thank you. Goodbye.'

She set off across the room, but he was before her, stopping her with one hand on her arm, his expression impassive. 'I think you should stay, Fiona.'

His touch sent fire through her veins. Proudly she lifted her head, staring at him with undisguised contempt. 'Why? I don't think we have anything to discuss, Mr Sutherland, and I'm quite capable of finding my way home safely.'

'Oh, but we do have something to discuss,' he said softly, ruthlessly. 'The woman at the employment agency told me that you had a son. A four-year-old son. You must have married very soon after we . . . met.'

Every vestige of colour left her face. 'I did,' she said, attempting to wrench her arm away.

His grip tightened, the fingers biting cruelly into the soft flesh.

'Married and widowed so soon? You've lived through tragic times since we last met, Mrs Ward. How did your husband die?'

She bit her lip, but the lie, so often practised, so often told, came easily to her lips. 'In a road accident,' she whispered. 'Let me go—you're hurting me!'

'I'm sorry.' His fingers relaxed, fell away from her arm, but he stayed close, his eyes watchful. 'I'd forgotten how easily you bruise.'

Stonily, her nerves stretched to breaking point, Fiona stared at the crisp white line of the handkerchief in his breast pocket. Every instinct urged her to flee, to take to her heels and run as if all the devils in hell were after her, but she knew that it would be useless. Adrenalin surged into her bloodstream. As flight was denied her, she must fight.

'I'm sure you had,' she said politely. 'I don't really feel like reminiscing. It's a pointless exercise, except for the very old, so let's call it a day, shall we?'

He laughed softly. 'Oh no, Mrs Ward, we shall not call it a day. What is your son's name?'

'Jonathan,' she said quickly. 'And he's not quite four.'

'Indeed? You must forgive me if I don't believe you. Do you know I have a fancy to see him. I'll take you home and meet him.'

'No!' The harsh monosyllable ripped through the air. Wildly she improvised, 'He's staying with a friend tonight.'

'A pity,' he said coolly. 'Who does he look like, you or his father?'

'Does it matter?' she demanded. 'I don't know what you're up to, but I don't have to stay here and listen while you probe into my affairs. Goodbye.'

As quickly as a snake his hand came out and snatched her handbag. 'Most mothers,' he said insolently, 'keep a photograph of their children in their bags. I know my mother always has.'

The clasp snapped open. As his fingers delved into the bag Fiona choked, 'Don't you dare! Don't . . .!'

One arm clamped to his side. With a rapidity that shocked her Logan tipped the contents of the bag on to the table, riffled through them with lean brown fingers, then twisted the wallet open. Fiona drew a ragged breath, kicked him hard on the shin and twisted away, but even as she reached out he held the photograph up and caught her back against him by the hair, holding a knot of it cruelly twisted in his grasp. Tears blinded her eyes. She sobbed once, then brought her hands up to the nape of her neck, trying to rid herself of his painful grip.

It seemed an age before he let her go. Once again she snatched at the photograph, but he evaded her, turning the coloured snapshot over to read what she had written on the back.

'Jonathan Logan Ward, aged four,' he said in a voice totally devoid of emotion, then tore the snapshot into pieces, letting them fall on to the opulence of the carpet. 'Jonathan Logan Sutherland, it should be, you little bitch!'

'I'll have to get another one taken off the negative,' she said dully, staring down at the scraps of paper. 'I only had the one.'

'Fiona—why?' His voice was coldly furious, his hands on her shoulders bit deeply. 'Why didn't you tell me?'

Fiona lifted her eyes. 'After what you called me?' she whispered. 'After what you did? Would you have believed that the baby was yours if I'd told you that I was pregnant?' Her voice trembled as she went on, 'If I remember correctly you called me a slut, a promiscuous, vicious little bitch—and that was before you really got going.'

'Of course I did.' He shook her slightly, then threw her away from him as though the touch of her defiled him. 'God in heaven, Fiona, I was furious! You were eighteen, and you fell into my arms like a ripe plum. I was twenty-six, damned well old enough to know better than to go to bed with a child scarcely out of school. How did you expect me to react?'

Wearily she pushed a hand through her hair, dragging

it back from the fine bones of her face. 'Well, it's all water under the bridge, isn't it,' she said tonelessly. 'I ... I realise it's come as a shock to you——'

'A shock?' he interrupted, breathing heavily; then more calmly, 'Yes, I suppose you could call it a shock. Sit down, Fiona. We have a lot to talk about.'

'We have nothing to talk about,' she said coldly. 'Nothing at all.'

'Don't be a fool,' he rasped impatiently. 'Of course we have to discuss this. You knew that I wouldn't just walk off and leave you once I knew about the child, or you wouldn't have fought so much to prevent my finding out about him.'

'Nothing has changed,' Fiona said desperately, afraid to the depths of her being. 'Jonathan is *my* son.'

'And mine,' he said quietly, then as she still didn't move to a chair he threatened, 'Are you going to sit down, or shall I make you?'

She bit her lip, turned, then began to weep, crying with an abandon that terrified her, yet unable to keep the tears back.

'God in heaven!' he exclaimed, then pushed a handkerchief into her hand and held her against his chest as she cried away the worries and fear and despair of the last five years. Cried because Jonathan had a father who would not let him die of bronchitis, and yet cried with contrary emotion because he was no longer entirely hers. At last she was spent, hiccoughing as she scrubbed her eyes and blew her nose.

'I ... I'm sorry,' she whispered, stepping back.

'So am I, but at least that's over and done with,' he said crisply. 'You'd better have some more brandy.'

'No ... no, thank you. I'm quite lightheaded enough as it is.'

In a gentler voice he said, 'You're just about dead beat, I think. Go into the bathroom off the bedroom to tidy up and I'll order tea for us. Then we can talk.'

The bedroom was big and opulent too, very neat. A travelling clock stood on the table beside the double bed, but that was all that denoted Logan's presence. In the bathroom Fiona drew a shocked breath at the ravaged countenance that peered back at her from the mirror. In all the years since she had loved and lost Logan she had never seen such despair on her face, not even when her parents had died so brutally two years ago.

Swiftly she washed her face, then combed her hair back from her pale forehead, before an intensive rummage in her bag produced her only lipstick. Cheap though it was, the coral pink suited her, giving her confidence for the battle ahead.

For battle it was going to be, she knew that, and though she was deliberately repressing both thought and emotion, she could not stop the shudder that ran through her at the thought of it.

'Only he shan't take you away from me, little love,' she whispered, as if her son was with her.

Logan was standing by the window when she came back, staring once more out at the grey, windy day, his expression bleak and shuttered. He turned as she came in.

'Ready for the fray, I see. You pour, Fiona. Those sandwiches are for you.'

'I . . . I am hungry,' she admitted slowly, sinking into an armchair. 'You have your tea without milk, don't you?'

'Yes.' He came across to sit down opposite her, taking the cup and saucer from her with the grave courtesy she had once thought so charming. 'Go on, eat up. You look as though you could do with feeding.'

'It's been a miserable winter,' Fiona excused her thinness, but the sandwiches were delicious; smoked salmon, paté and chicken, and she ate them with real appetite.

'You see, I remember what you like too,' Logan said softly. There was a long, tension-fraught pause, then he said, 'Tell me about him, Fiona. What's he like?'

Startled, she set her cup down, and for the first time looked directly at him. Superimposed over the mature good looks she saw Jonathan's baby features, so much alike that one glance at a photograph was enough to proclaim her son's paternity.

'He's big for his age,' she said softly, her mouth relaxing into warm curves. 'He cries when he's hurt, great loud roars, then picks himself up and carries on with whatever he's doing; he's very determined. Occasionally he has tantrums, but they're getting fewer and fewer, because he's learning to control his temper. He's very affectionate, very loving with people he knows. He's intelligent. He can read already, and count. He's——' she shrugged and spread her hands, '—he's Jonathan. A person in his own right, not a copy of anyone else, or a vehicle for hopes or dreams.'

A smile twisted his lips. 'Liar, Fiona. He's your hope, and the substance of your dreams. Why did you not tell me? Oh——' as she began to speak, '—I can understand at first. I was a brute, and you were too young to know that my anger was directed at myself, not at you. But afterwards—you must have known that I would have helped.'

'Yes, I suppose so.' Frowning, she tried to remember just how she had felt, all those years ago, when terror and shame had been the grinning companions she could not evade. Slowly, staring at her fingers, she went on, 'I ... don't know how I felt, really. You see, I loved you, and I thought that—that what—that our lovemaking meant that you loved me. I was very naïve, and very stupid. Anyway, when you were so angry I just fled, back to Mum and Dad. Then, when I found out that I was pregnant, I told them—oh, not who you were, but what had happened. They were marvellous. Dad wanted to get in touch with you, but I wouldn't tell them who you were.'

Logan said savagely, 'Your father should have insisted that you tell him. As the child's father I had some rights.'

She bent her head. 'I know, but I was too raw from your rejection to ... to see that. I didn't really think of the baby as anything to do with you, stupid though it may seem. It wasn't until he began to look so much like you that I thought of you as—as having any rights to him. And then—well, my parents were killed, and Jonathan was all I had. I was afraid that if you knew about him you might want to interfere.'

She looked up suddenly, but if she had hoped to surprise some emotion in him she was disappointed, for his expression was remote, as cold as the charity he would offer her—and she would accept, for Jonathan's sake.

'You do want to interfere, don't you?' she stated flatly.

'I have to, Fiona. You had no right to keep the knowledge of Jonathan's birth from me, although I can understand why you did. Obviously you need money, or you wouldn't have come for this interview. Why?'

Quietly she answered, 'It's not so much the money. It's Jonathan. He had a bad attack of bronchitis a few months ago and he's still coughing. The doctor says he needs sunshine and a country life. That was why—why this seemed such a marvellous opportunity.'

'I'm sorry.' Logan frowned, tapping one lean forefinger against his knee. 'There's no lasting damage?'

'No—oh no!'

'Well, I think we can give him his life in the country.' He said it blandly, leaning back in his chair to meet her astounded gaze with cool amusement.

'I can't work for you!' she exclaimed heatedly. 'Don't be so silly.'

'I wasn't meaning that. I suggest we get married. Five years too late, I'll grant you, but to coin a cliché, "better late than never".'

Fiona swallowed, completely unable to speak. Jerkily her hand touched her mouth, then fell to her side as she whispered, 'You must be mad. I couldn't——'

'You can and you shall, my dear.' He leaned forward, his expression intent and purposeful. 'It's by far the most sensible course of action, as you'll realise when you think it over. Apart from anything else, the child needs a family, a father. He's my son and I am responsible for him. I don't intend to have him suffer under the stigma of illegitimacy, so we shall have to marry. Oh——' as she gave him a horrified look '—it will be in name only, I promise you, unless you wish it to become a real marriage.'

'No!'

'I thought not.' Smiling cynically, he rose to his feet. 'Poor Fiona, you've suffered a lot for one night's folly, born of youth's hot blood and too much champagne. I can never make the past five years up to you, but I can ensure that your future is secure as well as Jonathan's. You owe him that, I think.'

Slowly, with increasing clarity, it was being borne in on her that there was no way of escaping him. Desperation coloured her voice as she objected, 'But . . . everyone will know. I mean—I'm sorry, Logan, but I couldn't face people who know all about the fact that I was stupid and foolish enough to—to love you too well,' she finished defiantly, averting her head so that he could not see her crimson cheeks.

'You have an old-fashioned turn of phrase, my dear, but I get your meaning. I have no intention of allowing anyone to know, except my mother, who will have to be told, but you needn't worry about her. Her one ambition for the past five years has been to marry me off, so she'll accept the situation, especially when she sees Jonathan. No, the story we shall put around is that we met and married five years ago, in spite of your parents' objections, but quarrelled and parted. You didn't tell me of Jonathan's birth because you were afraid I would take him away from you. We met again, and decided that the old magic still worked, so went on from there. It has the virtue of being correct in almost all of the details.'

'Why didn't you tell me about your marriage?' Fiona asked shrewdly.

He gave a mocking, cynical smile. 'Because it hurt my pride to have a woman leave me flat. There are many who will consider it perfectly in character for me to refuse to admit to my one failure.'

Fiona shivered at the flat note of disdain in his voice. She stared at him, seeing the difference after nearly five years, the lines that denoted a frequent expression of derision, the hardness that made his mouth even crueller than it had been when he had turned on her after that night which had begun in laughter and excited anticipation, continued to passion and ended in the humiliation that still scarred her emotions. Then he had been incredibly handsome, reckless with the power his looks and his wealth, but mostly his personality, gave him, and he had snared her heart and her body with effortless ease. Together their mutual recklessness and passion had made Jonathan, and it was he, the product of that youthful folly, who was important. Without any more thought she knew that she would marry him, this cold, calculating stranger with his twisted smile and hard eyes, who would embark on matrimony because he felt it his duty to do so.

Quietly she said, 'Very well then, but it's up to Jonathan. If he likes you, then we shall go ahead with it. Otherwise—no.'

He laughed, but there was little humour in the sound. 'You'll marry me if he screams every time he sees me. He's a Sutherland—I don't expect you to realise what that means until you live at Whangatapu, but he is entitled to more of life than you will ever be able to give him. So make up your mind to it, Fiona. Consider it to be Fate that we met again, foreordained, if you like. There's no escape for you or for me. Now, if you'll finish that last sandwich, I'll take you home. I want to meet my son.'

Fiona stood up, ignoring the last sentence. 'You can't force me to marry you,' she said firmly, trying to keep the thin note of fear from her voice.

'No? Don't you believe it,' he returned smoothly, though there was cold finality in the words. 'You haven't a hope, my dear. You may as well enjoy it, for you'll have to appear to be a devoted wife when we go north. I'll have no more gossip than is absolutely necessary. As it is, tongues will wag enthusiastically for a few weeks until some better subject for discussion comes along. Well, what are you waiting for? It's time to go.'

Logan's car was a hired one, not too big for easy parking,

but very luxurious. He drove well and efficiently, with the same controlled purpose which had taken over her life, his hands relaxed on the wheel.

At last he pulled up outside the big old mansion which was now a honeycomb of rented apartments, looking around with distaste.

'This is no place for a child,' he said coldly. 'Go in and get him. Tell whoever is looking after him that you're spending the night with relatives. Pack some decent clothes.'

'But—where——?'

'I have reserved a room for you at the hotel. On the way back I'll arrange for the marriage. That will give us three days to get to know each other. Then we'd better have a couple of weeks' holiday so that the child will become completely accustomed to me.' He slanted an ironic glance at her. 'And you, too.'

Jonathan was sitting in Mrs Wilson's tiny sitting-room watching the children's programme on television. He gave a squeak of joy when his mother came into the room, and jumped up to fling his arms around her.

'Hullo, darling.' Fiona kissed him lovingly.

'Mummy, I've been good. Good as good for Mrs Wilson. She cooked me a nice egg for lunch, and we drawed a face on it.'

He was so like Logan that her heart stopped for a frightening moment. Pray God he never developed his father's cynicism or harshness, Fiona thought fervently.

'I'm glad, love. Now you must thank Mrs Wilson and say goodbye to her.'

'Would you like a cup of tea, dear? How did the interview go? Do you think you got the job?'

Fiona flushed delicately as she met the faded eyes so filled with concern for her. Mrs Wilson was sweet, and alone in the world. She would miss Jonny, as she called him. Fiona could not lie to her. So she said quietly, 'Jonathan, go back and watch TV, darling.' When he had done so she continued, 'Something very wonderful happened today,

Mrs Wilson. The—the man who interviewed me was Jonathan's father. I'm not a widow, you see. I left him before he knew that I was expecting a baby, and I changed my name because I thought he might try to take Jonathan from me. He—he wants me to go back to him.'

'Oh, my dear child!' Mrs Wilson breathed excitedly. 'How ... how lovely for you—and for Jonny. But I shall miss you so.' She dabbed a handkerchief to her eyes, then resumed quickly, 'But of course you're right to go back. Jonny needs a father. When are you going?'

'He wants to get to know Jonathan first before we go north.'

'How wise and sensible. Are you happy about it?'

Fiona smiled, willing it to be radiantly happy.

'Yes, very happy, not only for Jonathan's sake, Mrs Wilson.'

'I'm glad, dear. You deserve to be happy and cared for. It's worried me to see you grow so thin and worried-looking. Do keep in touch with me, dear. I shall look forward to hearing about your new life.'

Touched, Fiona bent to kiss the soft old cheek. 'Thank you,' she said softly, then quickly, before the threatened tears came, she called to Jonathan.

He came, said goodbye and thank you to Mrs Wilson with grave politeness, then took Fiona's hand as they walked along the echoing corridor to their door.

'What are we having for dinner, Mummy?' he asked as she inserted the key in the lock.

'I don't know, darling.' Fiona pushed the door open, drew him inside and said, 'We're going to stay in a hotel tonight, Jonathan, so I shall have to pack our clothes. If I put your best ones on the bed can you get into them by yourself?'

'My longs and jacket that you made, and my good shoes? Yes, I can dress myself, Mummy.'

And he did, the tip of a small tongue between his lips as he buttoned and patted himself into shape. That little pink tongue was one of his endearing characteristics, denoting intense concentration. As she swiftly packed clothes into her one suitcase, Fiona felt her heart turn over. Any sacrifice would be worthwhile, if it were a sacrifice for her son!

Logan was waiting by the car. He straightened up and strode towards them, his face an impassive mask except for the leaping light in his eyes when they rested on the small face, a youthful mirror image, except that Jonathan's hair had some of his mother's copper tones.

As he took the suitcase Logan said softly, 'Have you told him anything?'

'No,' she breathed.

'Good.' He smiled down at his son. 'Hullo, Jonathan.'

'Hullo, man.' The clear childish treble was interested. 'Are we going wih you?'

'Yes. You can sit in the back.'

'With Mummy?'

Logan swung the case into the boot. 'No, I think Mummy should sit in the front so that she can see where we're going.'

Head tilted slightly to one side, Jonathan surveyed his father with unblinking eyes. It was not difficult to see that this was a summing up between the two males, nothing to do with Fiona except that she was the cause of it. Logan stood quite still, a curious half smile pulling the corner of his mouth, then, so quickly that Fiona almost missed it, the same quirk of the lips was seen on Jonathan's mouth.

'O.K.,' he said cheerfully. 'What's your name?'

'Logan. What's yours?'

A crow of laughter. 'You know, 'cause Mummy told you. I'm Jonathan Logan and I'm four years last birthday. Mummy is twenty-three last birthday and we had a cake with twenty-three candles. How old are you?'

'I'm thirty. In you go.'

He put them both in the car; Fiona unclasped her tense hands and turned.

'Don't bounce, darling. It's not Logan's car, so you must be extra careful of it.'

'Is he just having a lend of it?'

'Loan,' Fiona corrected automatically. 'He's hired it while he's here so that he can drive around in it instead of taking buses.'

'It's nicer than a bus,' Jonathan said amiably, and fell to exploring the ashtrays.

Fiona began to ask him not to, but Logan, who had by this time started the engine, said, 'Leave him be. He can't damage anything.'

'No, I suppose not.' She had changed into her best clothes too, a slim blue dress which was three years out of date, but which suited her although it was slightly too big. When she had looked at herself in the spotted mirror at the flat she had thought that she looked neat but not gaudy. Now, beside Logan in his expensive suit, she knew that she was incongruously out of place. Even Jonathan's clothes were too obviously home-made. The thought hurt, but she thrust it to the back of her mind. Logan might be rich, but it was not that which would win his son's affection. Jonathan had known nothing but kindness and love, and somehow she knew that Logan wished for the boy's love. For once in his life he would have to work for it, she thought wryly, for the splendid physical presence which made him almost irresistible to women would not have any effect on his son. She was not worried about Logan's attitude towards Jonathan. It was the thought of the enforced intimacy of a loveless marriage which fretted at her nerves.

Quite dispassionately she knew that it would be easy enough for her to surrender to the tug of attraction which still existed between them. At the hotel his touch had fired her blood, and she knew now what she had not known when she was a very immature eighteen-year-old, that men could feel sexual interest in women they did not even like. For all that his eyes had been cold when they rested on her, there were banked fires there, waiting only for a signal from her to flame into life. It would not be a hard one to give. Their brief desire had been a wonderful thing, a night of passion and surrender, giving and taking, joyous ecstasy in mutual fulfilment. That could be hers again, if she were insensitive enough to accept the needs of his masculinity instead of love. Fiona knew, without even thinking it through, that she never could. Not even to provide Jonathan with companions, not even to assuage the hidden needs that lay deep within her. That lesson she had learnt in a hard school, and she had learnt it well. The bitter taste of humiliation was never far from her memory.

'Are you worried about something?'

She said quietly, 'No, not now. Not any more.'

'Then stop frowning. It doesn't suit you. What time does Jonathan usually go to bed?'

'Six o'clock.'

Logan nodded. 'Is he restive at night?'

'No. Once he's asleep he stays that way until six the next morning.'

'Six?' He slanted a smile at her. 'He should go down well on the station. We're all early risers there.'

Thankfully she seized on the neutral subject. 'Tell me about it, Logan.'

'It's very old for New Zealand. The first Sutherland who came out found an area of land which had been entirely depopulated in the wars between the tribes and bought it. It's called Whangatapu, "Sacred Harbour" or "Forbidden Harbour", because the *turehu* were thought to live there, the fairy people. Ian Sutherland built a little *nikau whare* for his wife, and they lived in that for fifteen years while she had six children and he brought in the land. When they were wealthy enough to build a proper home he imported some stone workers from Australia and built himself a Georgian home out of the volcanic stone that forms one of the old cones on the property. That still stands, two-storeyed and square to the beach. It was added on to later, but my father pulled most of the gingerbread Victorian down, so that the lines are pure Georgian now. There's an acre of garden around it, my mother's domain, and the usual outbuildings necessary to a station. The three workers' cottages are about a half mile from the house, with the woolshed and yards, the implement shed and the forge halfway between.'

'How far is it from the nearest town?'

He shot her a sardonic look. 'Oh, it's not too isolated. About fifteen miles.'

'I see.' Ignoring the implied dig at her city-dwelling background she asked, 'When Jonathan starts school will he go by bus?'

'Yes. It comes to our gate. Picks the children up at eight-fifteen to take them to a two-teacher school six miles away. When he reaches Form One he'll go to the High School in Somerville, which is where we shop. There's a small play centre attached to the local school where he can go three mornings a week. Do you drive?'

'Yes, but I've had very little experience on gravel roads.'

'You'll soon learn. You can practise on the roads on the station before you tackle the real thing.'

A small black head with coppery highlights insinuated itself between them. 'Are we going to live with you, man?' Jonathan asked with interest.

'Yes. Do you think you'll like that?'

He pondered, finally answering sturdily, 'If Mummy likes it I will too, 'cause I like being where Mummy is. Where do you live?'

'A long way from here, in a house by the beach.'

Jonathan asked in eager tones, 'Do you live on a farm?'

'Yes.'

'With cows and sheep and dogs?'

'Yes, we have all those.'

A long silence, then so softly that it was clear he feared a rebuff, 'If there's a little dog without a friend, do you think I could be its special mate?'

Fiona turned her head in astonishment. She had not known that Jonathan wanted a dog, but there was no mistaking the wealth of longing in the childish tones.

'Why, yes, I'm sure you could,' Logan said after a moment. 'What sort of dog would you like?'

'I don't know until I see him.'

Logan laughed. 'Quite right, because the dog will have to choose you, too. We'll see what we can do. And I think you'd better stop calling me "man", now that we know each other.'

'What shall I call you?'

Silence, then Logan said coolly, 'You can call me Dad, or Logan, whichever you like.'

'Are you my dad?'

'Yes, I'm your father.'

'Mummy, is he my father?'

Fiona nodded, swallowing to choke back the great lump in her throat. 'Yes, he's your father, Jonathan.'

There was a hiss of expelled breath from the child, then he said in sedate tones, 'Well, that's nice. I always wanted my father, but Mummy said he was a long way away and couldn't come. I'm glad you came, ma—Dad. You can look after Mummy now. Mrs Wilson told the other lady that Mummy needed someone to look after her 'cause she was tired. Are you going to look after Mummy?'

'I certainly am from now on. What is that Mummy wants most, do you know?'

A mischievous chuckle was the prelude to his answer. 'She wants to buy me a train set, 'cause when I asked her for one she said she couldn't afford it and she cried in the bathroom. And then she wants books and records. She always stops to look at those shops, but I think she wants the train more.'

'Jonathan!' Fiona was horrified at such blatant cunning, but her son's eyes were laughing and bright, his mouth curved into a teasing smile, and beside her she felt Logan's body move as he prevented himself from laughing out loud.

'And that's quite enough of that,' Fiona said severely, shaking her head at the boy. 'Look, Jonathan, there's a dog. Would you like one like that?'

His attention distracted by the huge Borzoi towing its owner along the street, he watched it go by, climbing on to the seat to peer out of the back window after it. Finally he said, 'No, it's too big and hairy. I want a dog my size.'

'Fair enough,' Logan commented. 'Well, here we are.'

CHAPTER TWO

'Is he asleep?'

Fiona nodded as she came through the door. The room Logan had booked for her was right next door to his suite. She was grateful for the consideration he showed, not interfering in her arrangements to give Jonathan his dinner and put him to bed.

Judging by the array of papers around him he had occupied his time to some avail, but now he put them into a briefcase and stood up, eyeing her with cool interest.

'You look tired. I've ordered our meal for up here, and I suggest you get an early night. We have quite a lot to do tomorrow.'

'Such as?'

'Buying both of you some clothes, for one thing, and organising your removal from that—from your flat.'

She gave a bleak smile, sinking into a chair. 'You needn't pull your punches. I'm not ashamed of the flat, although it certainly doesn't come up to your standards. I wanted to talk to you about Jonathan.'

'Yes?' He was aloof, almost brusque. 'Have some sherry. I can see you screwing your courage to the sticking point.'

Fiona accepted the glass, but set it down beside her without tasting it. 'Logan, don't spoil him, will you?'

'Meaning what?'

It had to be said, though his reply was distinctly discouraging.

'Meaning that he's been very happy until now with very few material possessions. Don't allow him to feel that he only has to ask for something to have it given to him.'

'Fiona, because of you I've missed out on five years of my son's life.'

She paled at the bitterness in his voice. Like a mask of

teak his features were cold and threatening, but in a voice that was soft and even he went on, 'I don't blame you entirely for that; both your parents and I must share the blame, but the fact remains that he's a total stranger to me. I'm not so foolish as to think that I can buy his love, but he's still very young, and a few toys will help him to lose any constraint he may be feeling. You've done well with him, but you must have realised that he's growing to the age when a father becomes more and more important to him. Did you know that he wanted one—or that he longed for a dog?'

'No,' she murmured shamefacedly.

'So you don't know everything about him.' He smiled suddenly, and coming across the room he took her hands in his, drawing her to her feet. 'Your hands are cold. Are you afraid of me?'

'No. There's no reason to be, is there?'

His hand cupped her chin, forcing her eyes up to meet his, no longer ice blue, but alight with mockery and purpose.

'Don't you want to fall in love with me again?' he asked softly before he bent his head to kiss her.

His mouth was warm and hard, ready to take ruthlessly what she was not prepared to give him. Some deep instinct warned her to remain passive under his kiss, not to fight him even though every nerve shrieked danger, for that was what he expected and he would enjoy subduing her. So she lay quiescent as his mouth explored the fine contours of her face, tasting as though he was hungry for the satin-smooth skin.

'You're more beautiful than you were,' he said quietly against her throat. 'But so cold. Have you dug in behind a wall of ice, Fiona? Did I do that to you; drive all of that generous passion underground?' He laughed suddenly and released her. 'I wonder how long you can keep it up. Shall we bet on it?'

'No.' She strove for indifference, caught it around her like a cloak. 'It won't make any difference, Logan. I'm sorry, but if you want that sort of relationship you'd better go home without us.'

His eyes narrowed. 'Ah, I want my son more than I want you,' he said cruelly. 'But I'm quite sure that before long I shall have you both.'

'You never seemed conceited to me when I first knew you,' she returned, contempt colouring her tones.

'Answer me truthfully—one question, Fiona. Was that once when we made love the only time you've ever given yourself to a man?'

She stared, colour rushing to her cheeks. 'You have no right to ask me questions like that!'

'Answer it.'

'It's no business of yours,' she said indignantly. 'If you think I'm promiscuous——'

'You've answered me.' He smiled, but it did not reach his watchful eyes. 'No other man has possessed you. Well, that makes everything easier for both of us. Come on, drink your sherry. It will calm you down and give you an appetite for your meal.'

In later years Fiona could never remember much about the following days. Kaleidoscopic fragments, unrelated pictures were all that remained—buying clothes, Jonathan laughing with Logan on the cable car, a tantrum halted before it had ever really started by one word from Logan, old Mrs Wilson pressing a small goodbye gift into Jonathan's starfish hands, wind and rain and cold, and then the ceremony at the register office, Logan tall and withdrawn beside her as he put the wedding ring on her finger, and the lack of emotion in the obligatory kiss.

And then the plane trip up to Rotorua, the smell of sulphur and the plumes of the geysers; she and Logan slowly relaxing with each other as Jonathan proved an efficient go-between. Childish chuckles mingled with deep masculine laughter; the first time Jonathan demanded to kiss his father at bedtime: the first time he slipped his hand into Logan's as they walked along the street; his questions about his grandmother Sutherland: the telegram from Whangatapu from Logan's mother—the cold impersonality of the yellow slip of paper couldn't hide the bubbling excitement that had animated the composer of it.

And then, after three weeks, the air journey to Auckland, huge and sprawling on its isthmus between two harbours; a cup of coffee at the airport between flights and the trip in the amphibian up to Whangatapu, to arrive there in the quiet splendour of a warm spring afternoon.

From the air it was obvious that the station was a wedge-shaped peninsula, with a small round bite out of it on the northern side.

'Whangatapu,' Logan said.

'It . . . it looks lovely,' Fiona replied, swallowing.

He looked sharply at her. 'Nervous?' At her nod he touched her hand. 'You'll be fine. Don't worry.'

His consideration brought a pale smile to her lips, but something perilously akin to panic made her tense. For Jonathan's sake she must carry everything off with confidence, but her heart quailed at the thought of Mrs Sutherland and those others who waited in that white house below. On her finger gleamed the wedding ring Logan had bought for her, a wide gold band which suddenly looked far too new.

His fingers moved to clasp hers in a firm grip.

'Come on,' he said softly, 'you can do it.'

And so she did, climbing out of the Grummond on to the concrete slipway, walking up beside her husband as he carried their sleeping son towards the woman who stood there, tall and slim in dark slacks and a bright red coat with her hands stuffed mannishly in the pockets.

'Is he asleep?' she asked in curiously deep tones. 'Let me see, Logan.'

One long finger touched the child's flushed cheek tentatively, then Ailsa Sutherland smiled and looked at the slender girl standing a little apart. 'Welcome home, Fiona,' she said gently. 'I suppose you're dying for a cup of tea.'

'Yes—thank you.'

Logan's mother looked down at Jonathan as though she could not bear to be parted from him. 'I see he has something of you in him,' she said. 'Those red lights in his hair. Otherwise he could be Logan at the same age.'

As if unable to speak further she urged them up the gravel track from the landing ramp towards the house. Halfway along it Jonathan woke up as he usually did, all at once, and sat up in his father's arms.

'Ho!' he exclaimed awfully. 'Has the little plane gone?'

'Yes, I'm afraid so. The pilot was in a hurry to get back home,' said Logan.

Jonathan looked around interestedly. 'Where's this?'

'This is home.'

The bright blue gaze fell on the strange woman.

'Are you my grandmother Sutherland?' he demanded.

Huskily she replied, 'Yes, I am. You can call me Gran if you like.'

'Gran?' He rolled the word around his tongue, then gave her his charming smile. 'I like Gran. I had another Gran and a Grandy, but they went to live with God a long time ago, so I can't 'member them. You can call me Jonathan Logan Sutherland, if you like.'

'Hullo, Jonathan Logan Sutherland. But I think for every day I'll just make it Jonathan.'

'O.K. Do you live here too? Put me down, Daddy, I can walk.'

But once down he ran ahead, holding his arms out and making the high whining noise which denoted an aeroplane.

Ailsa Sutherland drew a deep breath as she watched him. 'He ... he ...' She stopped, reached out a hand and touched Logan before saying with a briskness which failed to hide how moved she was, 'You must forgive me if I dote a bit, Fiona. I shall try not to spoil him, but it will be hard.'

Deeply warmed, Fiona gave her a shy smile. 'He's not always charming, I'm afraid. Ask Logan, he's seen him screaming and stamping with rage.'

'Well, he should know how to deal with it,' his mother

observed. 'His temper can be fierce. But Jonathan is charming—totally natural and unaffected. He should settle down without any difficulty.'

Something in her voice told Fiona that Ailsa had some reservations about her daughter-in-law's ability to adjust quite as easily as Jonathan. But she would, she vowed. It was another thing she vowed to Jonathan.

The house was sheltered from the sea by a wide belt of casuarinas whose long green needles hushed gently in the slight breeze off the water.

'The forecast is for wind and rain tomorrow,' Mrs Sutherland said as she opened a small gate in the stone wall. 'But I don't need to tell you that, Logan.'

He smiled. 'No, I can smell it already.'

Fiona gave him a bewildered glance, then stiffened as he dropped his arm over her shoulders. Jonathan finished a wide circle, homed in on them and tucked his hand in Logan's, saying confidingly, 'I like this place. I'm glad we're here, aren't you, Mummy?'

'Yes, darling. Very glad.' It was strange to feel Logan's arm across her shoulders, but she knew that he was doing it for the sake of his mother and anyone else who happened to be watching, so she tried to relax.

The garden helped. Fiona loved flowers; her parents had been enthusiastic gardeners, but their small city section offered no such opportunities as this sub-tropical area.

She stopped and breathed 'Oh!', her eyes suddenly ablaze, for it was beautiful with the heritage of over a century of growth and loving care. Camellias glowed in a wide bed underplanted with great drifts of freesias whose scent hung heavily on the still air. A few late bees buzzed busily around a clump of purple lavender, while a tui preened in the topmost branch of a tall kowhai which was smothered in gold blossom. It was a formal garden, as befitted the house, symmetrical in proportions but so thickly planted it had an air of casual charm. And everywhere there was perfume, from the pink jasmine which draped itself lovingly across a pergola to the tiny blue spires of grape hyacinths. Stone paving and close-clipped lawns, two citrus trees in white urns, their fruit hanging like the golden apples of the Hesperides, finished off a perfect picture backed by the severely gracious lines of the house.

'What is that bush with the huge scarlet cones?' Fiona asked eagerly.

'A waratah, from Australia. Beautiful, isn't it, and the tuis love the honey. Listen, he's going to sing for us.'

Even Jonathan was still as the clear bell-like notes chimed in the quiet air. Up in his golden bower the tui's black feathers were shot with blue-green. The absurd bobble of white feathers at his throat gleamed as he lifted his head to praise the sunset.

It was almost too beautiful. A great surge of nameless emotion shook Fiona, so that she blinked back tears. And the tui seemed to have sensed this, for he finished the carillon with a superb imitation of an axe chopping into wood which set them all laughing, the tension gone.

'He does the men whistling up their dogs, too,' Mrs Sutherland said comfortably. 'There are bellbirds in the bush, but they sing later when all the other birds are silent. Look, there's Oaf. He lives in hope that he'll catch that bird one day.'

Oaf was a large rusty black cat almost the size of a fox terrier, who was carefully picking his way across the lawn towards the tree. When he heard Logan's voice calling him his ears pricked, but he ignored them with lofty disdain until the tui flew from the kowhai with a sound like ripping silk. Then he altered course and allowed himself to be scratched between the ears.

'Why Oaf?' Fiona asked, chuckling.

'No finer instincts. He lives for his food.'

Logan straightened up, took her arm and said, 'Come on, the dew is falling and we'd better get inside. If I know Jinny she's had the kettle on the boil for the last hour.'

'What's Jonathan doing?' Ailsa asked.

They all looked. Jonathan was standing under the grey

bole of a leafless jacaranda, eyeing the smooth branches with stern purpose. As they came closer he reached up an arm, hooked it around the lowest branch and pulled himself up into the crotch, grinning with sheer delight.

'Tomorrow I'm going to climb this tree,' he announced. 'Right up to its top!'

'You do that.' Fiona lifted him down, held him tightly against her for a moment, then set him on his feet. 'In the meantime, my lad, it's getting close to bath and dinner time.'

'Can I stay up late tonight? I had a sleep in the plane.'

Fiona opened her mouth, but Logan forestalled her. 'Just a little later than usual.'

This was one of the things that Fiona found it hardest to adjust to. She had been the sole arbiter of Jonathan's life for so long that consultation with anyone else seemed wrong, and she could not help a tiny flame of resentment whenever Logan made a decision for her.

It was something to be subdued. She nodded to Jonathan, allowed her husband to take her up the steps to the wide brick terrace and in through french doors to a room which was twice as big as her flat and furnished like an antique dealer's dream.

'We'll go up and get changed,' Logan said, 'then Fiona can meet Jinny and Tom.'

'Good. I put Jonathan in the guest bedroom next to yours. I thought he would be happier next door to you.'

'Good.' Logan lifted his head as the sound of an engine made itself heard. 'That will be Tom with the luggage. Show Fiona where to go, will you? I'll help him with it.'

Mrs Sutherland led the way out into a wide hall, up carpeted stairs and along another hall, watching Jonathan as he coped manfully with the stairs, a curious sad smile on her lips. It brought home to Fiona as nothing else had the enormity of what she had done and she said quietly, 'I'm sorry. I didn't realise, you see.'

There was no pretence at misunderstanding her. 'How could you, my dear? But you can't have known Logan very well.' She stopped before a door, saying slowly, 'He's not an easy man to live with, but for everyone's sake this must work out. I've never seen him so relaxed as he is with Jonathan.' The blue eyes, so like her son's, met Fiona's squarely to give emphasis to her next words. 'Forgive me if this seems harsh, but you must understand your position. We are all prepared to accept you for Logan's sake because of the child. There's a great deal of curiosity about you, of course. Logan is liked and respected through all of Northland; as his wife you will be looked up to, even envied. People expect a certain standard of behaviour and character from us. If you don't measure up then you'll have to go.'

Fiona blinked, hiding her emotions beneath her lashes. A cold rage gripped her, but she straightened her shoulders as she replied lightly, 'The gypsy's warning, in fact. Thank you, Mrs Sutherland.'

'I've made you angry, I know, but this had to be said; and believe me, Fiona, it's far better for me to tell you than to have Logan point it out.' She must have seen the involuntary contraction of Fiona's brows, for she nodded. 'Yes, you know what he's like when he's angry. It doesn't pay to arouse it. Here's your room, I'll leave you now.'

The room was large, as opulently furnished as the drawing-room, although in a far more severe style, but the first thing Fiona saw was the huge double bed. Almost she protested, but her lips closed tightly over the unsaid words.

Wait, she cautioned herself as she restrained Jonathan from running eagerly over the thick gold carpet. Quite obviously Logan had not told his mother everything about their marriage, but if he thought that by presenting her with a *fait accompli* like that sybaritic bed he was going to force her into his arms, he had another think coming! Sooner she would sleep with Jonathan, and he spent all night kicking out wildly!

Logan brought in her suitcase, dumped it on the floor and surveyed her narrowly, his eyes gleaming with saturnine laughter.

'I'm not sharing this with you,' she said, forestalling a

remark which she knew would be calculated to make her lose her confidence.

'But why not?' He moved across to it, pushing down on the cover. 'It's most comfortable, I can promise you, and you won't like dossing down on the floor.'

'I daresay I'd get used to it.' She moved over to unlock the case, determined not to be frightened. He could not force her to sleep with him, and she was not going to be persuaded into it, however much he poured on the charm.

'Why fight the inevitable? To salve your pride? Or to make me suffer a little for being realistic enough to know that it *is* inevitable? Do you want me to woo you romantically, with all the trimmings, so that we can pretend to be in love? Love is a romantic's dream, Fiona, you should know that.'

She swung around, her eyes stormy with anger, at that moment hating him for his arrogant confidence in his dark attraction. 'It is not inevitable,' she snapped, hanging on to her temper with great difficulty. 'You—you're so conceited that you think any woman who has shared your bed must want you until the end of her life! Well, my memories of any pleasure we got from each other are overshadowed by your reactions when we woke the next morning. I've had almost five years to think about my foolishness and your brutality, and the only conclusion I've reached is that I'm never again going to run the risk of repeating either!'

He laughed softly, not in the least impressed by words spoken in a fierce undertone so that Jonathan, who was busily exploring the built-in wardrobes, couldn't hear.

'He does rather cramp your style. I'll have to make sure he's around when you show signs of wanting to spit. Leave it—for now. Just remember, Fiona, that propinquity is a great seducer. And my patience is not inexhaustible.'

'You said—you promised that this was to be a marriage in name only,' she said in a hard voice.

Shrugging, he retorted coldly, 'I'm prepared to wait until you've got over your quite understandable desire to pay me back for what I said to you five years ago. God knows, I've learnt enough about women to know that they have a long memory for grudges and I'm quite happy to let you indulge yours for a while. But not for ever, Fiona. Jonathan needs other children in the family, and you and I are going to supply them for him, when you admit to yourself that this attitude of yours is an attempt to cover the fact that you want me as much as you ever did.'

Two patches of colour stained her cheeks as she stared at him with shocked accusation. 'You ... you *fiend*!' she exclaimed. 'You deliberately misled me! You ...'

'Oh, for God's sake come off it, Fiona,' he ground out impatiently. 'Stop playing the innocent! You must have known that I had no intention of living like a celibate after our marriage. What the hell do you think I am, half a man? Stop looking like Lucretia when she was confronted by her ravisher and get that boy ready for his meal.'

With shaking hands Fiona turned back to take out Jonathan's small pyjamas and dressing gown, his slippers and the old stuffed rabbit who lived on the end of his bed, striving for normality. Jonathan must not see that she was upset.

From behind her came Logan's voice, smooth and lazily insolent. 'You may recall little of the pleasure we had in each other, my darling, but I happen to have a rather better memory. You were very innocent, but what you lacked in experience you made up for in ardour and a great willingness to please. It will be like that again. And that's a promise, not a threat.'

Having to care for Jonathan helped. By the time she had bathed him and introduced him to his room, smaller but still very luxurious, and answered his questions, her pulses were steady, although the shadows did not leave her eyes. Logan had gone downstairs; she slipped into the bedroom and changed swiftly, washing her hands and face in the bathroom which led off it before making up carefully. One of her husband's gifts to her was a cosmetic case packed with everything a woman could ever need for armour. By deliberately concentrating on that she kept her mind calm.

'Well, how do I look?' she asked Jonathan, who had watched with absorbed interest.

He grinned, crinkling up his eyes. 'Pretty, like Daddy says. Can we go now?'

'Yes.' One last look at the smooth, very youthful face in the mirror, then she took him by the hand. 'Come on, we'll see where Daddy and Gran are.'

Logan was waiting at the foot of the stairs, lean and darkly handsome in a pale gold sweater above dark slacks. His eyes, hooded in the subdued light, rested unblinkingly on them as they descended the stairs hand in hand.

Then he said, 'Very pretty, Fiona, but hardly appropriate.' And she knew the mockery was there beneath the outward appreciation, for she had chosen to put on a pale green dress which gave her an untouched, virginal air.

Jonathan had his meal in the morning room, eating the crumbed cutlet and beautifully fresh vegetables with enjoyment while his elders drank sherry and talked commonplaces about Rotorua and the weather. Mrs Sutherland kept her hungry glance on him, as did the tall spare middle-aged woman who was Jinny, the housekeeper and cook. She had favoured Fiona with one keen, penetrating look, a smile which was just a movement of her lips, and then ignored her, which suited Fiona fine.

Tiredness and the discipline she was imposing on herself made her eyes heavy, so that she was content to sit quietly and savour her drink, listening as Logan talked to his mother about the affairs of the station, one eye on her son as he ate.

Halfway through his fruit salad he put down his spoon, yawned enormously, and sank against the back of the chair.

'Time for bed,' Fiona said softly, rising to her feet.

Logan picked him up. 'I'll carry him.'

Jonathan fell asleep almost instantly, sprawling with abandon between the sheets. Fiona bent, kissed his cheek, then left him, leaving the door open so that she would hear him if he did happen to wake.

They waited for her in the drawing room, mother and

son. As they turned to the open door she suddenly saw a likeness in them transcending the physical. They shared black crisp hair and blue eyes, chiselled bone structure, a lithe easiness of stride; but it was the air of authority, the rock-bottom confidence in themselves which she would never possess, against which she could batter herself in vain. What hope had she of standing against them?

The thought made her falter in her step. Instantly Logan stepped forward, taking her arm.

'You're just as tired as he is,' he commented. 'And I recommend the same medicine—early to bed. Here's your sherry—finish it and then we'll eat.'

'Did he go off to sleep?'

Fiona smiled at her mother-in-law's anxious query. 'Yes, like a log. He probably won't move all night.'

'Ah, that's good. I suppose you must all be tired. I wonder why travelling is so exhausting? Just sitting all day shouldn't set one yawning at six o'clock in the evening, but it always does.'

She went on chatting lightly, smoothly, occasionally with a caustic wit which stung but was not malicious. Fiona appreciated the motive behind the conversation and responded, but with the best will in the world she could not infuse much warmth into her voice. Mrs Sutherland's frankness at the door of that horrible bedroom upstairs precluded any sort of spontaneous response, especially as Logan was listening watchfully to all that was said.

At last dinner was served in the panelled dining-room. Superb food, superbly cooked, champagne as it was a special occasion, and then coffee and the scent of jasmine through the half opened window.

Outside it was night. A small wind had sprung up from the north and was busily fretting the long damask drapes, keening forlornly against a double-hung window at the end of the room. A pale moon rode high, its melancholy face veiled by fleeting clouds; there was a sudden spatter of rain against the windows.

'The weather is thickening,' Logan said, getting up to

close the windows. He slanted a look at his wife, almost lost in the depths of a dark green armchair, and went on, 'Time for bed, Fiona. You're just about dead on your feet. Say goodnight to Mother and I'll escort you up the stairs.'

Mrs Sutherland smiled. 'Yes, off you go. Sleep well, my dear.'

Obediently she said goodnight and preceded him through the door. His arm around her waist was unwelcome, but she knew better than to protest, and besides, her legs did feel woolly.

'I'll check Jonathan,' he said softly, outside the door to their room.

Inside it Fiona pulled the heavy drapes across the window and walked aimlessly back to her suitcase, refusing to look at the bed as though by avoiding it she could make it and all that it represented cease threatening her.

She pulled a nightdress out of the suitcase, a filmy rose concoction, and stood staring down at it blankly. Then, determination straightening her shoulders, she walked across to the bed and began stripping off the thick corduroy bedspread.

'Just what do you think you're doing?'

Logan's voice made her jump, but she continued, saying coldly, 'I'm making up a bed on the floor.'

In answer he came across the room, grabbed her wrists and held them firmly. 'Come with me,' he ordered curtly, urging her straight through the bathroom and into a small, monastically white room lined with cupboard doors. A single bed was pushed against one wall.

'This is where I'll sleep,' he said smoothly, releasing her. 'Until you're over your fit of the sulks.'

Relief made her angry. He had deliberately baited her, knowing that she would worry all through dinner about their sleeping arrangements!

Crisply she retorted, 'There's no need for you to move out. I can sleep here. And I am not sulking!'

'You'll be closer to Jonathan in the main room. And if you're not sulking you're giving a damned good imitation of it. No——' covering her indignant retort with his hand, 'you are tired, I'm tired, and I'm not going to listen to another foolish word from you.' His lips replaced his hand. The kiss was hard, totally without gentleness or respect, and it lasted for so long that the blood drummed in her ears.

'If you say anything at all,' he threatened against her mouth, 'I'll take you in that other bedroom, tear your clothes off and rape you. Now go to bed!'

Fiona stiffened, stared into his eyes which were half savage, half laughing, and gave a rueful smile. 'You're a tyrant of the first order,' she said, 'but as you're Jonathan's father I suppose I'll have to put up with it.'

'I'm also your husband.'

She walked back into the other room. 'It's as Jonathan's father that I think of you.'

'Well, I'm damned if I regard you exclusively as Jonathan's mother. You are also my wife. Don't ever forget that, for I have no intention of doing so!'

CHAPTER THREE

A CHUCKLE close by woke her up. Jonathan, Fiona thought, and smiled sleepily, back in the flat once more. A deep voice woke her fully.

'She'll wake up if you give her a kiss,' Logan told his son. 'Always wake a lady with a kiss.'

'O.K.' A light flutter of lashes on her cheek denoted a butterfly kiss.

'Hey, that's not fair!' she protested, grabbing his arm before he could run away. 'A real kiss, my lad, or I stay sound asleep.'

Jonathan giggled and obliged, kissing her with an ostentatious smacking noise which made her laugh. She tickled him, then as he squirmed, dropped a kiss on his forehead.

'It's raining outside,' he told her sadly. 'Daddy said we can go over to the shed and look at the tractors later. Can I wear my jeans?'

'Yes, you may.' She looked up; Logan was standing in the door of the bathroom regarding her sardonically, a towelling bathrobe open to the waist revealing that he had just showered. He grinned openly as she slid down the pillows, and rasped a hand over the night's stubble.

'I suppose I'd better shave before I kiss you good morning,' he mocked. 'Coming to watch, Jonathan?'

For some reason the sight of his father shaving had an irresistible fascination for Jonathan. He slid from between Fiona's arms and dashed across the room, demanding, 'Can I turn it on? Can I make it go bzzz?'

'You may.'

As soon as she heard the hum of the shaver's motor Fiona jumped out of bed, pulled on her slippers and a lilac quilted dressing gown and began to brush her hair. When the razor stopped the two males moved into the dressing room where

Logan had slept, so she went into the bathroom and snatched herself a quick shower. Goodness, she thought, soaping herself with some exotically named soap, this was absolute bliss, even if the weather had turned sour.

By the time they came back she was neatly clad in blue slacks and a pale grey lambswool sweater and was putting the clothes from the suitcase away in the empty drawers of the dressing table.

Logan caught her, kissed the nape of her neck and released her, all within the space of ten seconds.

'That smells nice,' he said. 'What is it?'

'Lily of the Valley. Logan, are these wardrobes for my exclusive use?'

'Yes.' He laughed at the wonder in her face. 'You'll fill them up and then say you have nothing to wear! And speaking of wearing, we'd better get our son dressed.'

'I've put his clothes on the bed. He can dress himself.' On an impulse she smiled at him, her slow sweet smile which had a hint of Jonathan's mischief in it. 'You smell nice, too.'

'After-shave lotion, called "Male", I believe. I have a fifteen-year-old cousin called Deirdre who keeps me supplied with it. Have you finished unpacking?'

'Yes, apart from Jonathan's few things. I'll stack them on the bed and then you can put the case away.'

All very domestic, as Logan heaved the case up into the cupboard on top of the built-in wardrobe, and Jonathan climbed into his clothes, humming the Wombles song cheerfully to himself. He had a clear, true little voice which made his father look at him.

'He obviously got his voice from you,' he said after a moment. 'I'm tone-deaf.'

'Are you?' In spite of the grey morning Fiona felt happier than she had been for weeks. Logan in this teasing mood was no threat to her peace of mind, unless it could be called threatening that he dominated the big room with his dark litheness, that aura of masculine virility which was so essential a part of him.

So she said pertly, 'Well, I'm glad you're not perfect. It gives me a little more confidence.'

'Oho!' he exclaimed, reaching out a long arm to pull her against him. His fingers found her chin, forced it up so that he could scan her face.

'It would be a perfect oval if it weren't for that square chin,' he said softly, tracing the contours with his finger. 'Don't try me too far, darling, or I might forget that I've promised to wait patiently.' He bent his head and kissed her.

At this opportune moment there was a knock on the door, heralding Jinny with a large tray.

'Oh!' she exclaimed, slightly flustered. 'I'm sorry——'

'Why should you be?' Logan grinned down at his wife's heightened colour before releasing her without haste. 'Have you brought us up tea, Jinny? Bless you, but you have enough to do without pampering a lazy layabout like Fiona.'

'I thought she might like to lie in, seeing it was her first day,' Jinny reproved him.

'Thank you very much.' Fiona was glad that she had pulled the bed back ready to make and plumped the pillows up: Logan wanted this to seem like a real marriage, and certainly no one would realise that they hadn't shared that big bed.

'Have you got time to have one with us?' Logan asked.

Jinny shook her head. 'No, Tom's going to be yelling for his eggs any minute, so I'd better go.' She turned to Fiona. 'I've made porridge for Jonathan, oatmeal. Does he like that?'

'There are only two things he dislikes,' Fiona answered. 'Broad beans and parsnips, and those he flatly refuses to try, even. He'll eat anything else you care to give him. Can I help you with anything?'

She knew immediately that she had made a mistake. The thaw that had seemed to set in iced over in an almost palpable withdrawal that put her firmly in her place.

'No, thank you, I'm well enough organised to cope on my own,' the older woman returned brusquely, and left the room with a stiff back and head high.

'Why?' Fiona turned in bewilderment to her husband.

Logan shrugged. 'She and her husband have been here for twenty years, and she's had her own way for most of that time. My mother is not the most domesticated of creatures. I think Jinny is probably making sure that you realise her position here.'

'Oh, I see.' But she found it hard to realise that the housekeeper might be so set in her ways that she would disdain help freely offered. It appeared that even though she was Logan's wife her status in the household was ambiguous in Jinny's eyes.

'Just go easy for a while,' Logan advised her. 'She's a bit stiff, but if you make a friend of her you'll never find a truer one.'

'It takes two to make friendship a real thing,' Fiona said mildly, fighting down something close to desolation in her heart. It seemed that the corroding loneliness of the past years was not over, even though her surroundings had changed so much. Then her eyes fell on Jonathan, seriously buckling his belt, and she knew that it would all be worth while. The people of Whangatapu might never accept his mother, who was supposed to have walked out on his father in a fit of pique, but they were prepared to take the innocent one to their hearts, and for that she could endure anything.

It was a miserable day. There were periods of sunshine, when everything looked fresh and newly washed, but these were followed very rapidly by a blasting north-westerly wind which brought vicious squalls of rain and claps of thunder.

After breakfast Logan retired to his study and Mrs Sutherland organised Fiona back to the bedrooms to finish unpacking, sweeping Jonathan off with her—to give his mother some peace, she said. Fiona smiled. It seemed that even her brutally frank mother-in-law could indulge in a little self-deception when it suited her, for it was quite obvious that she wished to further her acquaintance with her newly found grandson, and had no care at all for Fiona's peace!

By midday the two rooms were immaculately tidy. Fiona had found a carpet sweeper in a hall cupboard and used it, then made the beds and cleaned out the bathroom, arranged all of Jonathan's toys around his room and topped up the water in the vases.

For several minutes she stood at the windows, staring down at the garden which had been so beautiful the evening before. It was still lovely, even though the sky was grey and rain scudded across it in great drifts, subduing the colours and tossing the branches about in a frenzy of action.

Was it the weather which made her so miserable? Come to the winterless north, she thought with a wry smile. Well, it certainly was nowhere near as cold as was normal in Wellington, but this was supposed to be spring! The sky began to lighten in the east even as thunder rolled around the hills to the north. Somewhere a blackbird sang, clear and cheerful.

Perhaps, she thought, that was to be her life here. She had not been able to prevent herself from building high hopes on the move to Whangatapu, even optimistically thinking of it as a chance to start anew. Like most high hopes, they would not be realised in full. Mrs Sutherland had made it painfully clear as to her standing in the homestead, and Jinny's attitude reinforced the impression that she was only here on sufferance. Why should she expect more? Foolish to have hoped that Logan's mother would be like her own mother, kind and gently compassionate. Among the circle in which her husband's family moved there might be some she could call friend, though the world of the very wealthy was a closed one to her. If there was not—well, there was always Jonathan.

Downstairs was as quiet as an empty home. Fiona hesitated for a moment at the bottom of the stairs before making her way to a door pointed out by Mrs Sutherland in the course of a sketchy tour of the house that morning.

The music room was not very big, separated from the

drawing room by great folding doors, but it held a grand piano. Colour touched Fiona's pale cheeks. This too, this gift she possessed, could give her ease and comfort of spirit.

Tentatively at first she played some simple pieces, then drifted into her favourites, some of Chopin's sparkling waltzes, a few of the haunting Russian composers, playing anything that came to mind. Apart from an old upright which Mrs Wilson owned it was the first piano she had played since her parents' death and, oh, she had missed it so!

At some time Jonathan crept in to stand beside her, watching silently as he loved to do, his expression as absorbed and remote as hers.

A long time later, it seemed, Ailsa Sutherland touched her on the shoulder. 'It's almost lunchtime, and I'm sure you must be hungry after all that playing.'

'I ... why, yes, I think I am.' Fiona wondered if she had been given a gentle hint that an hour of piano music was too much. The conversation over lunch intensified the feeling.

Mrs Sutherland said, 'Did you hear Fiona playing, Logan?'

'Yes,' he smiled across the table at her. 'I like the Rachmaninov. You'll have to practise to regain your technique, though.'

Fiona could accept criticism when it was justified. 'That's a lovely piano, Jonathan will love it.'

'Can he play?' Mrs Sutherland looked horrified, glancing at Jonathan's starfish hands as though expecting a piano to materialise at the end of them.

Fiona chuckled. 'Yes. He picked out tunes before he was two and I've taught him since then.'

'I should have thought he was too young to learn,' his bemused grandmother said a little helplessly.

Logan shot a look at her. A smile twitched the corner of his mouth. 'He can read too,' he remarked casually, his eyes laughing straight at Fiona's.

She bit back an answering smile, waiting for Mrs Sutherland's reaction.

'Good heavens! Did you teach him?'

'Yes, when he wanted to learn,' Fiona said calmly, refusing to allow herself to be ruffled by the older woman's obvious disapproval.

'I always thought it was bad to force children,' Mrs Sutherland said briskly. 'It isn't natural for children to read before they're five, surely. Perhaps he just knows his little books off by heart,' she concluded hopefully.

'Why is five the magic age?' Logan enquired, while Jonathan demolished his grandmother's theory by turning over his bread and butter plate and reading the manufacturer's mark slowly but clearly.

'Really!' Mrs Sutherland gave the child beside her an astounded glance, then smiled reluctantly. 'And there was I thinking he was a nice normal child,' she said, shaking her immaculate head. 'I can see I shall have to be careful what I say.'

'Little pitchers have big ears,' Jonathan observed cheerfully.

There was a stunned silence, then Fiona said in her calmest voice, 'Do you think we could go across to look at the machinery straight after lunch, Logan? I notice that the sky looks clear.'

'I don't have a sleep any more in the afternoons,' Jonathan told everyone. 'Mummy, can I wear my new gumboots?'

They walked through squelchy grass towards the group of buildings by the stockyards which were sheltered from the wind by a row of tall macrocarpa trees. Underneath them the ground was bare with a thick mulch of needles. Jonathan ran ahead, chuckling and calling against the wind, the tassel on his knitted cap streaming away behind him as he darted across to the white rails of the horse paddock.

Fiona eyed the animals with some trepidation. They looked unkempt in their woolly winter coats, huge and haughty and dangerous, but Jonathan gazed without any fear, and when a chestnut stepped delicately up to them he held out the piece of carrot that Logan had in his pocket and laughed aloud as the horse took it gently from him.

'Don't you like horses?' Logan asked, amused.

'Well, I always think a bicycle is safer and quicker.' Fiona watched her son carefully, but made no attempt to stop him from leaning out into the paddock. She looked up, met Logan's eyes and flushed. 'I try not to inflict my likes and dislikes on him,' she said quickly.

'Don't be so defensive. You've done very well with him, and given my mother considerable food for thought as well. Can't you ride?'

'No, and unless you think it absolutely necessary I'd sooner not learn,' she said firmly.

'Well, I do think it necessary, because I'm sure that once you lose your fear you'll enjoy it. Unless you're really terrified?'

She smiled reluctantly. 'No, I'm not. Why do you have so many, Logan? I thought everyone rode around their sheep on a motorbike now.'

'I prefer horses. There are quite a few areas on the place which are too steep for anything but a horse. Look.' He turned her to the east, pointing out where the peninsula rose to a jumbled heap of hills and spurs and gullies, most of it bush-covered. 'That's an old eroded volcano, Puiamumu, or the volcano of the valiant warrior. You can't get a tractor or a farm bike up much of that.'

'No, I can see that!' His hand rested lightly on her shoulder, irritating, yet pleasantly warm even through her heavy jacket. For something to say she asked, 'Have you ever climbed it?'

'Lord, yes. The first time when I was about eight. There's quite an easy track to the top.'

'You must get a magnificent view.'

'Yes. Up and down the coastline for miles, and almost across to the west coast. Hey, you little devil, where do you think you're going?'

He grabbed Jonathan just as he was about to launch himself into the horse paddock holus-bolus.

'To get the little horse—see, the baby one. Can I have it, Daddy?'

'That, my child, is a very old, bad-tempered Shetland pony, and you cannot have it. Now listen, Jonathan. You are not to go into this paddock unless I'm with you. Understand?'

'Yes, but . . .'

'Understand, Jonathan?'

There was a clash of wills. Jonathan stood gazing fearlessly up at his father, his mouth mutinous. Once he sent a pleading glance to Fiona, but she shook her head.

At last, scarlet in the face, he capitulated. 'All right, I won't, I promise. Why, Daddy?'

'Because some of those horses are not used to children and you might frighten them. I'll teach you to ride, don't worry. Now let's go across to the machinery shed.'

That was vast, packed with a bewildering array of vehicles and implements. Jonathan, of course, loved it. After the first five minutes Fiona sat herself down on the footrest of an enormous scarlet tractor and listened to their voices as they wandered around, her eyes fixed on the green swords of the flax bushes by the stream which wandered across the flats. The sun was shining and she was out of the wind, so that she began to get hot and more than a little sleepy. Lashes drooping, she let her mind go pleasantly blank.

The crunch of footsteps on gravel woke her. A man came striding up to the shed, shoulders hunched against the wind, his hands thrust into the pockets of his windcheater. He was young, with longish fair hair and a swaggering walk emphasised by the tightness of his jeans. When he saw her he stopped and openly stared, frank pleasure evident in the smile that curved his lips.

'Well, hello!' he said softly, coming up to lean on the huge rear wheel of the tractor. 'And who might you be? No, don't tell me. You're the boss's wife whom we've all been dying to see ever since we heard of you, five years too late.'

'I'm Fiona Sutherland.' Fiona knew that her voice was

primly sedate, but she didn't like the appraisal in his smile or the open insolence of his words.

'Wow! If you'd been my wife I'd have made sure you didn't take off so soon after the wedding.'

'Do you want Logan? He's in the shed somewhere.'

He grinned, totally unsnubbed. 'You can't put me in my place. A cat may look at a king, or so they say, and this cat has every intention of looking at you whenever he can. Where's the boy?'

'If you mean our son, he's with Logan.' She turned her head as their voices came closer. It may have been her imagination, but Logan's stride seemed to lengthen when he saw who lounged against the tractor.

'Hi, Logan. I've just been making your wife's acquaintance.'

Logan's cool glance rested a moment on Fiona's face, then shifted to meet the gaze of the younger man. 'Danny, take a look at the little Fergie, will you? It looks as if some idiot has cracked the sump. Come on, Fiona, rain's on the way. We're going to have to run if we want to get back to the house dry.'

But run as fast as they did, the rain beat them to it, and this time there were hailstones in it, little ones that stung the skin and brought tears to Fiona's eyes. Jonathan was safe. Logan was carrying him beneath his raincoat and when the hailstones hit he turned his face into his father's chest and clung like a barnacle, yelling, 'Giddy-up! Giddy-up, Daddy!'

'Whew!' Fiona leaned against the wall of the back porch, chest heaving, cheeks scarlet beneath her wet hair. 'What atrocious weather! Is it often like this up here?'

Logan grinned. 'We've had three weeks of it, so Mother tells me. It's normal; spring is the most unpleasant season we have. This is just more unpleasant than most.'

From the doorway came a sweet drawl tinged with malice. 'But not for you, Logan, surely? This must be a time of great joy for you.'

Logan swung round, his expression watchful, his mouth

controlled. 'We were talking of the weather, Denise.'

As he performed the introductions Fiona felt the other girl's eyes on her. No warmth in those brown depths, no welcome at all, although they seemed to soften when they fell on Jonathan, who stood staring up at the stranger as if bemused.

'Hi, Jonny,' Denise Page said charmingly. 'Been having fun?'

'Yes. You look like the princess in Snow White,' he said breathlessly. 'Just like her.'

And indeed, there was a distinct resemblance to the picture in his favourite book of fairy tales. Denise was tall and slim, elegant in a pale pink trouser suit of superfine wool, with long black hair caught back to show a face of extreme beauty. She was a thoroughbred, with an air of nervous delicacy, yet there was strength in those slender hands and wrists, for her handshake had been firm, almost masculine in feeling.

'Why, Jon, that's the prettiest thing anyone has ever said to me,' she laughed, dazzling him with her smile. Her lashes lowered as she gave Logan what could only be construed as a flirtatious glance. 'He really is a chip off the old block, in more ways than one. You'd better come inside and dry yourselves off, my dears, or you could catch a chill. It's turned very cold.'

There was a bathroom just inside the back door, where Logan could shower before he entered the house. Fiona dried Jonathan down, rubbed a towel over her head and face and then said to Logan, 'I'll go up and change us.'

'Right. I'm dry enough.' He was curt enough to make her wonder exactly what his relationship with Denise Page had been before he saddled himself with an unwanted wife.

Ten minutes later she opened the drawing-room door. A tinkling laugh and Mrs Sutherland's deep tones told her where they waited. Taking a deep breath, she led Jonathan in.

Mrs Sutherland was seated in her favourite chair by the crackling fire, working at an exquisite embroidery picture.

Logan and Denise Page were standing to one side of the fire, facing each other, the girl laughing up into his face as he smiled at her. All three of them looked at home together, as though they were completely attuned. She and Jonathan were the outsiders; then he ran ahead and leaned against his grandmother's knee, and it was Fiona who was the intruder, the outsider.

'I was just telling your husband that he's a sly one.' Denise remarked charmingly, moving a little away from Logan as Fiona came up. 'No wonder he's never succumbed to any of our wiles! You must know, Fiona, that he was the most pursued man in Northland; all the girls were after him! Not fair not to tell us you were unavailable, Logan. I think you enjoyed the hunt. Confess it, now.'

'You exaggerate, Denise.' He was cool, perhaps a little snubbing, for a gleam of something that could have been spite glinted in the girl's eyes for a moment.

It vanished, however, and she said, 'I don't, but I'll agree that it wasn't a tactful thing to say. What lovely hair you have, Fiona. I thought of rinsing mine that colour once, but I decided that it was far too artificial looking, so I never did it.'

If that was a dig, Fiona decided to ignore it. She did not like the girl, but she was not going to become embroiled in a game of 'highest score'. So she smiled, and allowed Logan to put her into a chair, folding her hands in her lap.

Denise's eyes missed nothing. 'Why you aren't wearing an engagement ring!' she exclaimed. 'I never thought you would allow your bride to be without that token of your affection, Logan. Or did you get married so quickly, five years ago, that you had no time to buy one?'

'My grandmother's is away being made smaller,' Logan returned quietly. 'Are you cold, Fiona? Would you like a hot drink?'

'A marvellous idea.' Mrs Sutherland put her work into her embroidery bag. 'Come on, Jonathan, we'll go and make some tea for your mother.'

'Do let me take him.' Denise smiled, taking Jonathan's hand. 'I haven't seen Jinny for a long while, and I must have a chat with her. She promised to give me her recipe for tamarillo chutney. I don't know what she puts in hers, but mine never tastes as good.'

'We'll all go. I know what will happen if you and Jinny start swapping recipes—we'll never get our tea. Fiona, get closer to the fire, dear. You look very pale.' Mrs Sutherland swept out of the room closely followed by Denise and Jonathan, still handlinked.

A long silence, then Logan said abruptly,

'What did Danny Harmon say that upset you?'

'Why do you think I was upset?'

'I've seen that look on your face before.'

Shrugging, she answered, 'Oh, nothing really, I just didn't like his attitude. Does he work for you?'

'Yes, he's the son of a friend of my father's, and is spending a year with us to gain experience before he takes over a fat lamb place in Hawkes Bay. What didn't you like about his attitude?'

Fiona was in a quandary. The last thing she wanted to do was create any trouble between Logan and his work force. 'He . . . well, he just seemed very young and brash.'

'He is young and brash,' Logan said deliberately, 'and he hates my guts. If he can do anything that will harm me he will. The sole reason that he came up here was just that—to create trouble. Oh, not in his work. He's farmer enough for that, I'm thankful to say, but he isn't trustworthy in any other way. So have as little to do with him as possible, Fiona. He's clever, and he's ruthless, and he's definitely not stable where I'm concerned.'

Fiona stared. The flat tonelessness of his voice forced belief, but she found it hard to credit what Logan had said.

'Why?'

He frowned, his features sharpened into a mask of complete detachment. 'It's a stupid story, and one I'd rather not talk about, but he'll find the opportunity to tell you, so you'd better hear the truth from me. Danny has a sister, a twin sister. We met three years ago, when she was twenty. She thought she'd fallen in love with me. When I realised what had happened I was possibly less tactful than I should have been, but she has some of Danny's instability, and to put it bluntly, she wouldn't take no for an answer until I spelt it out in a form even she couldn't mistake. She married another man on the rebound.'

'And Danny hates you because of that?' Fiona couldn't believe that.

'Oh yes. You see, the man she married is my brother Stephen. He and Mary live sixty miles away at Punere. When Steve found out that he'd been a substitute he proceeded to give her hell. Stephen was a great friend of Danny's. I get the blame for the break-up of that friendship, and for Mary's unhappiness and for Stephen's.'

'He *must* be unstable,' Fiona said quietly.

Logan shrugged, stirred the fire with the toe of his shoe and bent to put another log on. 'Thank you for the vote of confidence. It's only fair to add that I was pretty brutal to her.'

'Yes, I can well imagine it.'

He gave her a twisted smile of mockery. 'Just as I was to you, only then I was angry with myself so I really pulled the stops out. But you stole quietly back home to lick your wounds in private. Has it ever occurred to you that if you'd played your cards right I would have married you then?'

'What sort of marriage would that have been?'

'The same sort as it is now.'

The glow of the lamp tangled copper explosions in her hair as she shook her head. 'No, because this is for Jonathan. Giving him security makes this—this mockery of a marriage worthwhile.'

'I hope you think so ten years from now,' he said sombrely. 'There will be no divorce for us.'

'I hadn't . . .' Her voice trailed away into nothingness, for their glances clashed and held until a gleam of desire banished the hardness of his. He smiled, and came towards her, pulling her out of the chair into his arms. Resistless, she stood quite passive as he held her against him, her softness yielding to his rock-hard strength.

'You're still cold,' he murmured. 'Cold as ice, yet you have the lips and the colouring of passion. Kiss me, Fiona.'

'No . . .'

'Then I'll kiss you.' He kissed her without tenderness, his mouth sensuous and demanding, using all of his expertise to win some response from her.

Her heart speeded up, thumping erratically as her body proved treasonable, betraying her physical response to him. When his mouth left hers crushed and pleading, scarlet in her cold face, he said coolly, 'How much longer do you think you can keep up this pretence, Fiona? You know damned well that you want me, and God knows, I've proved that I want you.'

'Lust is no base for marriage.' She said it defiantly, willing herself to remain quiescent under the touch of his hands at her hips and breast. The aftershave he had used that morning teased her nostrils with its faint scent mingled with the clean male smell of him. His skin was smooth against hers, slightly damp, as revealing of his desire as his mouth and the slight thickening of his voice.

'When there's nothing else, it provides a stepping stone to better things,' he returned, closing her eyelids with his kisses, pulling her hard against him with hands which were cruel against her waist. She opened her mouth to protest, and was lost in the urgency of his kiss. All thought fled; she clung to him, holding his head between her hands, unable to control the needs she had kept subjugated for so long, moving against him in a simulation of the passion he wanted from her.

When at last he lifted his mouth from hers satisfaction gleamed deep within his eyes, turning the frosty blue to a flame, and yet there was laughter and understanding there too, so that she could not be angry with him.

'What fools we mortals be,' he quoted softly, teasingly. 'You and I both, Fiona.'

'Why you?'

'Because it would be so easy to take you, without caring for the scruples your romantic heart puts in my way. If I told you that I loved you would you believe me?'

'No,' she whispered.

'Must I make you believe it before you give in?'

It would have been so easy to say yes, to allow him to woo her in due form, to remember only that he could be a tender passionate lover—so fatally easy. Her eyes filled with tears for all that might have been.

Logan gave a smothered exclamation and kissed them away, saying, 'Don't, Fiona, please. I'm a brute to tease you. I promise I won't force the issue at any time. When you're ready we'll make this a real marriage, but not before.'

She gave a tiny choke of laughter. 'I can just see it happening, can't you? How would you like me to tell you? By letter?'

He grinned, tapped her cheek with a hand that stung slightly before releasing her. 'You can make the running this time, darling.'

'And join all the others who've chased you so unavailingly? Not on your life!'

Her reference to Denise's remarks made him frown, but he kept his tones light as he responded, 'Just drift along, Fiona. Take things as they come. Propinquity is a great help when it comes to easing over the rough spots. I may not be what you'd hoped for in a husband, but I think that when you're more used to me you'll find me a pretty fair substitute for your knight in shining armour.'

A silvery peal of laughter from the hall made them step further apart, as if they were guilty lovers. Logan grinned, and Fiona could not prevent the smile that touched her lips, still scarlet from his onslaught.

'You look very kissed,' he commented teasingly, 'but it suits you.'

'You'd better wipe the lipstick off.' She laughed at the dismay in his expression, and took her handkerchief to wipe away the slight pinkness against his lips. A moment later the evidence was removed, but the door opened, and before she could put some distance between them he curved his arm around her narrow waist, dropping a kiss on the top of her head.

'Hey now!' Denise laughed again as she carried the tray across to one of the tables. 'I never thought to see you canoodling in public, Logan. Fiona, what have you done to him? What magic is it that brings our aloof, proud Logan to show his heart so blatantly?'

'Hardly public,' his mother said drily, but her glance was not unsatisfied as Fiona, flushed and acutely self-conscious, moved away from Logan's restraining arm.

'Far more public than usual,' Denise said merrily. 'And here we were thinking that our tea would warm you, when all you needed was a cuddle from your husband. What's it like being an old married man, Logan? A far cry from the freedom of your bachelorhood, I'll bet. Oh, but I forgot, you were married all along, weren't you. How silly of me—and how tactless.'

It was quite obvious what she was trying to do. Fiona found that the thought of Logan kissing other women was distasteful, but she was more interested in just why Denise Page was subtly implying the fact that she, at least, had known what it was like to be lost to the world in Logan's arms. There was nothing to be learned fom the other girl's face; it was guileless, but there was no warmth in the dark eyes, merely a surface glitter which hid any emotions. Fiona could not rid herself of the uneasy feeling that Denise was following some plan she had formulated—and that she knew the truth about their marriage, and was making sure that Fiona realised it.

During the next half-hour, as Denise talked and laughed, dazzling Jonathan with her manner and her charm, Fiona watched quietly for signs of any tension between her husband and the girl. Logan, of course, gave nothing away, and Denise very little, but however careful a mask she wore she could not prevent her eyes from seeking Logan's, her voice from deepening when she addressed a remark to him. And even if there had been no sign, there was the slight frown on Mrs Sutherland's brows to reveal that she was watchfully alert, ready at any time to step in if she felt uneasy about the course the conversation was taking.

'Are you usually as quiet as this?' Denise asked Fiona, smiling just a little too teasingly.

Logan answered, his voice warming as he said, 'She's a very restful soul, Denise. And her son talks enough for three.'

'He's a darling.' There was genuine, unexpected feeling in the light voice this time. As she spoke Denise hugged Jonathan against her, smiling into his face. 'I hope you aren't a possessive mother, Fiona, because I would love to get to know him properly. I was thinking—you know I take Evelyn Dickinson's two children into Play Centre at the school once a week, Logan, on the morning that I spend with the Spinning Circle. Would you like me to collect Jonathan too? He would love the Play Centre, and it will be good for him to know the children he'll be going to school with. I'm a very safe driver, Fiona. Tell her, Logan.'

'She is—very safe.' Logan's glance was thoughtful as it rested on the child against Denise's knee. 'What do you think, Fiona?'

She had expected him to make the decision himself, and was touched by the way he deferred to her. 'I think it's an excellent idea,' she said quietly. 'We'll give him a couple of weeks to get used to being here, and me a chance to become accustomed to driving on gravel roads, then I'll take him in the first couple of times. It's three times a week, you said, Logan, didn't you?'

'Yes, Mondays, Wednesdays and Fridays.'

'The Spinning Circle is on Wednesdays,' Denise interpolated.

'Then thank you very much.'

Denise positively sparkled. 'There you are, Jonny. Do you think you'd like to go to Play Centre with me?'

Jonathan yawned, covering his mouth guiltily, before saying with sleepy pleasure, 'Yes, thank you, Denise.'

'Jonathan!' Fiona looked at him severely, but Denise

hurried into speech before he could be scolded.

'I asked him to call me that, Fiona, he's not being impertinent, so don't be cross with him.' She touched his cheek affectionately. 'I think this business of being so formal with one's elders is terribly old-fashioned. If you insist on him calling me Miss Page I shall be very sorry. Please don't.'

Fiona looked at Logan, who nodded.

'Ah!' Denise cried, intercepting their silent communication. 'Your lord and master has permitted it, so you can't deny me. You know, folks, I must get up and go. We're having people to dinner tonight, and I still have the flowers to arrange. My mother will be on the telephone any minute. Mrs Sutherland, when are you going to give a party to introduce Logan's wife to the district? It's too long since you had one of your fabulous "do's".'

'In a few weeks,' Logan's mother said briskly. 'When Fiona knows us here a little better. And though I don't want to hurry you up, Denise, if you want to get home before another hailstorm, I suggest you go now. Take a look at that cloud!'

It was purple-black and moving fast, shot with stabs of lightning. Denise gave a squeak of mock terror and ran, calling goodbyes behind her as they followed, Logan moving fastest, so that he put her into the bright red Maxi that stood on the gravel circle outside the front door.

As she came through the door Fiona saw him, bending down to listen to something Denise was saying, his dark features intent but stern, close to the girl's vivid, laughing loveliness. She said something, touched his cheek as he straightened up, and was in the car and away, a spatter of stones from the wheels making tiny splashes in a puddle as it swept out across the cattle stop. The horn sounded, a pale pink arm waved goodbye and the little car fled across the flat and up towards the road.

CHAPTER FOUR

'FIONA,' called Logan, 'I've a pile of typing for you to do. Can you break the back of it this morning?'

Fiona smiled and walked in through the study door, a great sheaf of camellias in her arms.

'How much?' She gave the pile of papers on the desk one glance and raised her brows in mock horror. 'Have you given an indication as to the answers?'

'Yes. The three on top are the most urgent, but I'd be glad to get the others away today. Where's Jonathan?'

'Riding his trike around the circle. He's only had it three days, but I'm sure the tyres can't last out much longer.' She paused, then said joyfully, 'He hasn't coughed for a week. You should bottle your air and sell it.'

Logan grinned, allowing his eyes to rove meaningly across her face, and down the length of her body. The day was hot, as great a contrast to the bleakness of a fortnight before as it could possibly be, and to match it she had put on a slim cotton dress in her favourite shade of pale green. The northern sun had kissed her arms and slim legs to a pale gold, and begun its work of bleaching the dark copper hair.

'It certainly hasn't done you any harm,' her husband said smoothly, observing with sardonic eyes the delicate flush that stained her cheeks. 'You look good enough to eat in that outfit.'

For a moment as their eyes caught and clashed, tension sparkled in the air between them, then he turned, and said abruptly, 'You'd better get rid of the flora if you're going to do this. Can you get them done today?'

'I should have them finished by afternoon tea time.'

'Good.'

The camellias were destined for a big white urn in the

hall, where their warm ruby red would repeat the impact of the carpet against the white wallpaper. Fiona worked quickly but to great effect; this and keeping their rooms tidy were the only things Jinny allowed her to do in the house. Stifling a sigh, she supposed she really would not have time for much more, for Mrs Sutherland, who wrote detective novels, was well away on her latest, and Logan kept her busy with office work.

She had never realised just how much paper work there was to do on a big farm like this. Apart from all the stuff directly concerned with Whangatapu, there were articles he wrote for journals, logs and diaries to be kept, notes on his experimental herd of Santa Gertrudis cattle, and an immense correspondence that was worldwide. He seemed to belong to a vast number of organisations, not all of them connected with farming, as Fiona discovered one day when a letter from a child he was sponsoring in Greece came to the house. He did not tell her, but when she came to getting the files in order she discovered letters from two other children, one in Bangladesh, the other in Hong Kong. They touched her as his care of Jonathan could never have done, and made her realise just how little she knew about this tall, enigmatic man who was her husband.

After that first day he had been aloof, almost withdrawn, behaving towards her with courtesy but no hint that he had ever expected or wanted closer association than that of growing friendship between them. No flame of passion showed in his eyes, he made no further attempts to kiss her or hold her, and though his arm was frequently around her waist or across her shoulders this was only when there were people to observe it. Against her will Fiona could not help being piqued by his indifference; it did not help matters that she knew that this was exactly the reaction he intended to arouse in her.

Sometimes the comment he had made about her making all the running popped into her mind, and she wondered if this was what he expected her to do. But at other times, when he was all that a companion should be, she acquitted him of trying to out-manoeuvre her and was grateful for his consideration and undemanding courtesy.

And certainly, he could not have been better with Jonathan. It warmed Fiona's heart to see them together, the tall man and the sturdy boy, to watch Jonathan fall headlong into hero-worship of this superb father of his who was teaching him to ride a spirited pony, who took him out fishing in the runabout, and who never once assumed that anything Jonathan wanted to do he was too young to try. There was respect in their relationship, too. Jonathan learnt that one glance from his father's eyes was as cutting a punishment as any words or physical chastisement could be. Fiona was glad of this; for some time she had known that her son needed firm masculine discipline and she welcomed his response to it.

The respect was reciprocal. Logan did not talk down to his son, or treat him with the affectionate but stifling disregard for his maturity that Jinny, for example, was inclined to adopt when she spoke to him.

Jinny ... Fiona sighed as she set the urn straight on the narrow console table. Jinny loved Jonathan because he was Logan's son. Logan's wife she treated with a rigid respect which was in itself a negation of regard, ignoring any attempt on Fiona's part to come to a warmer relationship.

'You have a way with flowers,' Mrs Sutherland said from behind her. 'Fiona, can you do some typing for me? I've re-written half of the third chapter and all of the fourth.'

'I have some stuff to do for Logan, but it shouldn't take me long. I'll get yours done by dinner time.'

'Oh, don't make a slave of yourself. I'll tell you what, I'll take Jonathan out with me after lunch. I'm going to see the Pages—Lilian hasn't been too well lately. When I was talking to Denise on the phone last night she said that she needed someone to cheer her up, and Jonathan certainly does that. That will give you a clear afternoon.'

'Fine. I'll have plenty of time to do it if I'm uninterrupted. Is he still riding that tricycle?'

Mrs Sutherland's face relaxed into what could only be called a doting expression. 'Yes, bless him. He must have ridden miles on the thing. He's settled in marvellously well! He's so like Logan when he was the same age, determined and fearless. Logan was always the leader. Stephen followed along behind, imitating his brother like a small shadow, never quite succeeding as well as Logan. I often used to wonder if it was because they were so close in age; there's only fourteen months between them. It used to worry me, Stephen's hero-worship, but he grew out of it, of course. Logan is the one with the strong character. Stephen is not exactly weak, he's enough Sutherland to prevent that, but he will always be a follower.' She smiled reminiscently, then a quality of sadness crept into her expression. 'Has Logan told you about Stephen and Mary?'

'I know they're not particularly happy together,' Fiona said quickly, hoping to forestall any confidence. Somehow she felt that she could not bear to listen to that pettily tragic story again.

'No, I'm afraid Mary is like her brother, unstable. And yet it was Stephen she was fond of before she conceived that stupid crush on Logan, and it was Stephen she turned to after—when it ended. I'm sure she loves him. Unfortunately Stephen can be bitter when he feels let down by someone he loves. They're very well suited, if only they would realise it and stop wallowing in self-pity.'

'I'm sure they'll work something out. After all, they wouldn't have stayed together for so long if life was completely hellish, would they?'

But Mrs Sutherland refused to be comforted with platitudes. 'I don't know. Stephen is possessive, like Logan. I'm afraid he's quite capable of using any affection Mary has for him as a weapon.'

Fiona looked her horror. 'You're describing a—a domestic tyrant!'

'No, my dear, merely a man who's always been a little jealous of his brother; who hasn't come to terms with the fact that his wife used him as a refuge. It will be interesting to see how they react to you. In fact, you know, I'm hoping that the news of your marriage to Logan might act as a sort of catalyst, breaking the ties of the past so that they can build afresh.'

'Are they coming here?' Fiona most emphatically did not want them here, disturbing her tenuous peace of mind.

Astonishment raised her mother-in-law's beautifully plucked brows. 'Didn't Logan tell you? They're coming across next weekend for the party, staying over Saturday night. Stephen is lucky that he has an excellent man who's quite capable of looking after the farm if he goes away—Stephen goes away, I mean.'

'Oh! No, Logan hasn't told me.' Fiona gave a wry smile. 'No doubt he thought I knew.'

'Well—we have been talking of it, Jinny and I, but I suppose it was when you weren't around.'

Mrs Sutherland sounded doubtful, as if undecided whether to apologise, then her shoulders lifted in a slight shrug. 'Never mind,' she continued briskly, 'you know now. What are you going to wear on Saturday night?'

'I haven't decided yet.'

'Let Logan choose for you. He has excellent taste and knows just how you should look.'

Ailsa would have been both bewildered and horrified if she had caught even a glimpse of Fiona's mind as she made her way back to the study.

Let Logan choose indeed! she fumed silently. As if *she* couldn't be trusted to decide for herself what one wore to a party! How dare she! What—what complete arrogance these Sutherlands indulged in!

Logan, glancing up from his desk as she marched in, saw stormy grey eyes and flushed cheeks. His eyes narrowed, but he said nothing, merely watched as she sat down at the typewriter and began work. After a few moments the flush died down; a secret, very mischievous smile curved the wide, generous mouth, then she settled down to work properly.

One black brow lifted in Logan's face, but he too had

work to do, and for a long while there was so sound in the room but the clacking of keys and the rustle of paper. From outside came the trill of a bird, and if one listened carefully there was the ever-present hush of small waves on the shore. The harbour lay blue and serene under the spring sun, a far cry from the gunmetal grey aspect it had worn on the afternoon after their arrival at Whangatapu. Perfume from the great bed of freesias intermingled with that of the jasmine which climbed a pergola outside the window, teasing their nostrils with a heavy, sensuous fragrance. On such a day summer seemed almost there.

'What does this mean?' Fiona handed a letter across.

Logan looked perplexed, black brows drawn together as he perused the offending notes. 'I can't even remember writing that. Oh—yes, of course. It's the chap from a machinery firm wanting to arrange a field day here. Suggest they get in touch with the local Farm Advisory Officer—that's his name and address—and arrange it with him. It will have to be an open day—I won't allow Whangatapu to be used to promote one manufacturer's products. But a field day might be a good idea if the Advisory Officer cares to oversee it.'

'O.K.'

Half the letter had been written when the mellow note of the gong announced lunch. Logan muttered, 'Damn!' but he got up and held out a hand to Fiona.

'Come on, we'd better be there on time. Jinny hates her food to be kept waiting.'

Fiona made a small grimace.

Nothing escaped Logan. As he took her hand in his he said coolly, 'You still don't like her, do you?'

'It's rather hard to like someone who's so very disapproving,' Fiona murmured. 'Not that I blame her, mind you.'

'Oh, that's very forbearing of you. Why don't you blame her?'

She laughed up at him, that gleam of mischief glinting in her smile. 'Because all she knows about me is that I left you. And Jinny can't imagine why anyone should want to leave you for any but a discreditable reason, as you're so obviously perfect in every respect.' She primmed her mouth, but her eyes laughed at him above the gravity of her countenance.

'If I believed you ...' he paused, then said quite calmly, 'Well, I don't want her upsetting you. I thought she would come round to having you here, begin to treat you as my wife, but if she can't then she'll have to go.'

'I think that's a bit extreme,' she said objectively. 'Home help is extremely hard to get in New Zealand, and Jinny is a real treasure. She doesn't upset me. Actually, she has the kind of dour integrity that I admire. So don't say anything at all, because she'll think I've been making trouble, and that will be no recommendation of me to her. She loves Jonathan, and that's the main thing.'

He shot her a curious, rather hard look. 'Is that all you care about? That Jonathan's life should be happy? Don't you ever think of yourself as anything other than his mother?'

'Why yes,' she returned, 'I'm me. But I don't have to prove myself to anyone. At the moment Jonathan is the one who needs me. As long as he does that I'll be here.'

'Do you have to be needed so much?'

Fiona gave him a straight glance, aware that he was intrigued by her coolness towards him. No one could ever call Logan spoiled, but it was obvious that he had met with very few rebuffs in his life. The feminine half of the population adored him, because he was handsome and tall and had that magical magnetism, and men liked him too, for his integrity and because he was possessed of the indefinable quality which made some people leaders, while the lack of it doomed others equally handsome and magnetic, to be followers. At the moment he was playing a waiting game, giving her time to become accustomed to the idea of being his wife, with all that marriage implied, but she knew that impatience was also a part of his nature.

Occasionally she wondered whether his cool calculation

would give way to that impatience; but she was not particularly afraid. He would not take her by force, and she knew that her defences were sure and strong, for she had tumbled headlong into love with him again, only this time she would be content with nothing less than his love. And love was certainly not what he felt for her now; her deepest instincts told her that. Some part of it was passion, some pique, and the desire to own completely what was his. And some, she thought, a residual tenderness for the child she had been, and regret for the years when she had been forced to grow up so suddenly, bearing his child, caring for him without a husband to support her. A complex man, but she was a complex woman, and she could not be satisfied with an evanescent passion. If ever she gave herself to him it would be in the full knowledge of his love for her, and to win that love she was prepared to take on the world if necessary.

So she said lightly, 'Every woman needs to be needed. I thought that was lesson one in the sophisticate's manual, Logan.'

He nipped her arm with hard fingers, hurtful yet restrained. 'And you know all about it, I suppose? Well, we'd better not continue this fascinating discussion any longer, or Jinny will loathe the sight of both of us. But I intend to pursue it at a more convenient time.'

The purposeful manner in which he spoke made the words a threat. Fiona wondered just when he would choose to re-open the subject, but was not particularly worried. Fragile she might look, but she had deep inner resources and strength which constant use had intensified, so she was not afraid of anything that might confront her here. At least, she thought wryly, these people expressed their dislikes in a civilised manner!

Later that afternoon she had changed her mind about that. Denise Page had come back with Mrs Sutherland, and had set herself out to denigrate Fiona in a way which was as subtle as it was clever, so that all Ailsa saw was two girls talking together. Fiona paled besides Denise's vivid, tantalising beauty; became a shadowy, insubstantial creature with no character, no colour except that crown of copper on her small head. Even Jonathan seemed to prefer Denise.

The moment Mrs Sutherland had left them alone Denise said coolly, 'Shouldn't you be having a bath now, Jonathan? It must be getting close to your dinner time.'

'I have a wash before dinner and a bath before I go to bed,' Jonathan informed her. 'Would you like to give me my bath tonight, Denise?'

Open triumph gleamed in Denise's dark eyes. She looked across at Fiona, and said with more than a hint of complacency in her silvery voice, 'Don't you want your mother to bath you?'

Jonathan chuckled, a delightful baby sound, oddly at variance with the exquisite formality of the drawing room. 'No, not tonight.'

'Miserable shrimp!' Fiona retorted in tones of the deepest disgust. This was a game they often played together; it amused her that Denise was completely serious about it.

'Mummy is cross if I splash,' Jonathan went on triumphantly, and settled back against Denise, smugly waiting to see if his mother would rise to this lure.

'Jonathan hates having his face washed,' Fiona retorted.

'When I bath you, Jonathan, you can splash all you like,' Denise interposed neatly.

Fiona hid a grin. This was going to be entertaining. Granted permission like that Jonathan was quite capable of drenching everything in the bathroom, but Denise would have to discover that for herself!

At this moment Jonathan caught a glimpse of his father riding past on the big bay he called 'Taniwha'—Maori for Devil. With a gleeful look of defiance at his mother he hurtled out of the french doors and down the terrace, his jean-clad legs carrying him rapidly towards his hero.

There was silence in the big room. Denise leaned back into her chair with the relaxed motion of a cat, ran her fingers through her dark curls and said with light malice,

'He seems to be growing away from you, Fiona. Does it hurt to have him transfer his affection so rapidly?'

'Hurt? No, why should it?' Fiona's voice was vague as if she was not attending to the conversation, but her brain was working coolly. Right from the start she had known that Denise disliked her; now she was to find out why. Fiona thought sadly that she already knew.

But Denise apparently was not ready for this yet. She gave an exclamation which sounded very close to one of contempt, then asked, 'And how do you like living here? It seems to have done Jonathan the world of good, but I can't say the same for you. Have you always been so pale, or do you need iron pills?'

'I've always been pale. It goes with the red hair.' There was a thread of amusement in her voice which was not lost on the other inhabitant of the room.

A flush flamed crimson in Denise's cheeks. Losing her temper, she said roundly, 'It must have been the hair that caught Logan's eyes, then, for there's not much else to! I suppose you realise that if you hadn't turned up so conveniently he and I would have married?'

'He could hardly have married you when he was already married to me.' Fiona's lashes drooped deceptively over her eyes, hiding her thoughts. Oh, Logan, Logan!

She did not miss the impetuous movement the girl made, nor the rigid exercise of self-control which suppressed a retort.

Instead Denise replied, 'Well, he was in love with me—and I with him!'

So she knew about the hasty marriage, but was not as yet ready to use her knowledge. Fiona felt a sudden compassion for her. Spoiled, lovely and right in every way, Denise had probably met the first setback of her life when Fiona and Jonathan appeared at Whangatapu as wife and son. That she wanted Logan was obvious from the raw need in her voice; Fiona was almost certain that she wanted the position as chatelaine of the homestead even more. She must have been very sure of achieving her desires; perhaps Logan had

had an understanding with her, albeit an informal one.

About his emotions towards the girl Fiona was not certain. Even a man of his formidable self-control would have shown some signs of his repressed love, and there had been none, not the merest flicker of an eyelash or tightening of a muscle to denote tension when Denise was near him. And she could not help but feel that he was just not the sort of man to fall wildly in love with a girl like Denise who was quick rather than intelligent and for all her surface glitter a rather shallow person.

Perhaps she was underestimating the opposition, she thought sardonically. Certainly she was beautiful enough and her radiant confidence enhanced her suitability to be considered the ideal wife for Logan.

With that air of vagueness she could assume at will Fiona murmured, 'If that is so, I feel very sorry for you.'

'You?' Denise dismissed this with an arrogant jerk of her head. 'I feel sorry for *you*! You may be his wife, but I'll bet he didn't waste one moment of any of the years you spent apart thinking about you. And he ignores you most of the time even now—it's quite obvious that he wanted Jonathan and had to put up with you as part of the deal.'

Fiona's hand clenched a moment on the arm of her chair. Distressed by Denise's venom, she said quickly, 'I think this is a rather undesirable conversation. Let's end it, before anybody goes too far.'

'You really are a wishy-washy character!' Denise, confident again, allowed herself to relax, saying contemptuously, 'All right, we'll end it—for now. In lots of ways I'm rather like the Sutherlands, you know. I take what I want.'

'That's fine, if you're prepared to pay the accounting,' Fiona said sombrely, remembering that other occasion when she, too, had wanted, and had taken ... and the reckoning which seemed likely to ask a lifetime's payment.

But Denise, supremely arrogant as only youth can be, laughed mockingly. 'Oh, I'll pay gladly. The rewards will be immense, you see.'

*

The words still echoed in Fiona's ears. A full night's sleep had not managed to release her from the implications of them, especially as the evening that followed them re-inforced Denise's proud claim to their accuracy. She had scintillated brilliantly, a glittering girl in her favourite rose pink and silver, and her colour had risen as she effortlessly became the centre of attention. It was as if she had deliberately set out to show Fiona what she had to combat; she was a charming guest, and yet more than a guest, for Mrs Sutherland had invited two old friends of hers up, an artist called Forrest Thurston and his wife, and with Ailsa's warm support Denise had become a kind of secondary hostess.

The Thurstons were the least artistic-looking people Fiona had ever seen. Short and stout, they appeared more like brother and sister than husband and wife, and they looked as though they would be far more at home on a farm than before an easel. Mrs Thurston was a skilled and creative painter on china, while her husband had gained himself an international reputation as a portraitist of great perception and technical skill. Fiona was a little awed by them at first, but within minutes their pleasant homeliness put her entirely at her ease. Forrest teased her gently, made her laugh with some tales of the people he was asked to paint, and commented on the quality of her laughter, his too-perceptive eyes keen as they surveyed her.

'Hesitant, elusive, yet oddly compelling. You should laugh more, my dear. When you do, I see the real Fiona.'

His words had dropped into one of those silences which fall in any gathering, and it was Logan's lazily amused voice which replied to him.

'Her laugh was the first thing that caught my attention, Forrest. We met at Coronet Peak in the South Island when we were both skiing. She came a massive cropper just in front of me, and when I got to her she was laughing in the snow. Her cap had been thrown off and her hair was fanned out across the whiteness. I've never forgotten.'

He came across and touched a lock of hair by her flushed

cheek, smoothing the silkiness with what must have seemed a loving touch. It jarred Fiona unbearably, but she forced herself not to flinch away from him and the memories he had invoked.

'The true copper,' Forrest had said, 'so lovely and so rare. Did you know that copper is the metal of Venus, the goddess of love?'

There had been another little silence, then from Denise a trill of laughter and the words, 'And to think we always thought red-haired people were bad-tempered! How nice to have Aphrodite's colours, although she was a lady of somewhat questionable morals, if I remember correctly. At least she wasn't dull.'

Now as she leaned on the bar of the gate high above the sea, Fiona wondered why the malice in Denise's remarks hadn't been obvious to everyone else in the room. Perhaps because they were uttered with a charm that only Fiona knew to be spurious.

The sun beat sensuously down on her bare arms and face, hypnotic, drugging her into a state of semi-somnolence which was delicious but time-wasting. Behind her, to one side of the gravelled road which bisected the property, was the green car which Logan had bought her a week or so ago. It was the reason why she was two miles from the house in this silent place where the skylarks carolled a hymn to spring and the only other moving things were sheep drifting aimlessly across the close-cropped paddocks.

Fiona was rather proud of her skill with the car. It handled well, and after the first time the thick gravel on the road held no terrors for her, for Logan had explained exactly how to cope with it. And it brought her such moments as these, when she could be alone and off her guard completely, lost in the wide expanse of wrinkled sea, the misty haze of the islands on the horizon and the sheer sybaritic pleasure of sun and air so fresh that it was a shock to a city-dweller's lungs. Everything at the homestead seemed a long, long way off, small and remote and unimportant, even the nagging ache that had become a part of her since she had once more given her heart into Logan's keeping.

At times it seemed that she must give in to the whole-hearted urgings of her blood and become his wife with no strings attached. Foolish to cry for the moon, to be so naïve as to demand love as a requisite for their union! And yet ... and yet ... If she did, if their marriage was based on passion, it would only be as strong as that passion, and once it was assuaged what would there be left for them? Embers of a flame which could die as quickly as it flared, the bitter taste of ashes in her mouth. He had said that she owed Jonathan a father, and because she had to agree with that, she had married him.

But she owed Jonathan more than a father, she owed him the gift of parents who respected themselves and each other, and once she relaxed her guard against casual desire then her self-respect would be gone, and with it, she knew, any regard that Logan had for her. She was not afraid of unfaithfulnes, for he had exchanged vows with her and he would live up to them. What she feared more was being taken for granted, and the despair that would give her.

She had told Logan with pride that she was herself, not just Jonathan's mother. She knew that if she gave him what he wanted he would see her as his wife, not as Fiona, a woman with character and brains and talents, a woman who could never be content with the sinking of her individuality to become an extension of the Sutherland ego.

So ... the silent secret of tug-of-war between her and Logan must go on. He had reason and logic on his side, she had only the intuitive knowledge of a woman's heart, and that was frail armour for the struggle.

'Daydreaming? Or indulging in pride of possession?'

The voice from behind, totally unexpected, produced an unusual reaction in her. She jumped, and gasped before turning a face temporarily drained of colour to the man who had walked silently up behind her.

Danny Harman's taunting expression changed to one of

real concern. 'Hey, are you all right? I didn't mean to scare you.'

'Well, you did,' she said, snapping the words out, then had the grace to look ashamed. 'I'm sorry, I wasn't expecting anyone. How did you get up here?'

'Left the horse down by the creek when I saw you and walked up, but not, I repeat, with the intention of frightening you. I thought you might like some company.'

Fiona hesitated, Logan's warning foremost in her mind; but standing there in the sunlight he looked merely young and rather eager, not in the least dangerous. So she smiled, that slow smile which promised so much more than it revealed, and said lightly, 'I should be on my way back, or Logan will think I've gone over a cliff somewhere.'

He cast a professional eye over the car. 'How do you like her? Easy to drive, aren't they?'

'Very. I like it very much now that I've got over the butterflies in my stomach. It's quite a while since I've driven.'

'Umm.' He kicked the tyre, bent down to examine it and nodded. 'Must be nice to be able to buy the wife a new bus like this whenever you want. Lucky Logan. And lucky Mrs Sutherland. It's been almost a Cinderella story, hasn't it. Or so they say.'

The glance he gave her was taunting, a not-so-delicate probe to see if he had struck home. Fiona felt a surge of anger, but controlled it.

'Do they?' she said vaguely. 'It must be boring to have so little to do that one must gossip to fill in the time. If you'll excuse me, I'd better go.'

'Back to Logan?' He grinned jeeringly, lowered himself to the ground against the wheel of the car and looked up at her with deliberate insolence. 'If you go now you might run me over, and you really can't afford to have any more gossip circulating about you, you know. For one thing, it might make Logan think that bringing you back here wasn't such a terribly good idea after all. He's used to praise and respect from his peers and inferiors, not sly innuendoes and laughter that ends abruptly when he comes into the room. It must gall him to be on the receiving end, for once.'

He was casting for a rise, trying to bait her into—what? An indiscreet anger, some retort to feed his hatred, perhaps. Fiona did not intend to give him anything he could make use of, so summoning all her self-control she said quietly, 'Don't be foolish, Mr Harmon. It's too nice a day for dramatic confrontations.'

An ugly glitter in his eyes warned her that she had made a mistake.

Without moving he said silkily, 'I am not your precious Sutherland son, Mrs Sutherland, to be coaxed into reason by the threat of Mummy's displeasure. I've been waiting quite a while for this moment, ever since I saw you, and you're going to stay here until I say what I've come to say.'

Fiona lifted her shoulders in a shrug. 'Say away, then; no doubt it will be good for you to get it off your chest.'

He laughed, leaning his shoulders back into a more comfortable position against the car. One hand tilted the straw hat he wore to a rakish angle; with mocking deliberation he picked a long grass shoot and bit it with strong white teeth, his pale blue eyes fixed on her profile.

'I suppose your husband has got in first, and told you his version of the facts. Well, Mrs Logan Sutherland, you can hear the truth, and I hope it chokes you. Or perhaps I don't; you aren't to blame for what your husband did in the years when he acted the bachelor, secure in the knowledge that he had a wife tucked away somewhere if any of his girl-friends proved too importunate. For girl-friends, read mistresses, because I'm very much afraid that Logan was not faithful to you while you and he were separated.'

He paused, but no muscle moved in the slender figure, there was no change in her aloof profile.

'He seduced my sister,' Danny said conversationally. 'Seduced her, and when he got tired of her, got rid of her by marrying her off to Stephen. She, poor fool, thought that it was all right to sleep with the man she was going to marry. I could have told her that Logan's type doesn't marry lovesick girls with more looks than sense, but I wasn't here. I didn't get here until it was all over and she and Stephen were busy making each other miserable.'

He got to his feet, brushed grass from the legs of his jeans and straightened up, his glance seemed to scorch the air between them. 'In a way, Mrs Sutherland, I'm rather sorry for you. Like me, and Mary, you're here on sufferance. No friends, no position but that of Jonathan's mother; a husband who's half in love with the delightful Denise Page. You're too soft for the Sutherlands, so you'll get hurt, just as Mary got hurt. And there's no one to look after your interests, is there? You're quite, quite alone. Goodbye, Fiona, I'll see you at the party.'

Fiona watched as he strode off down the hill, shoulders high, swaggering slightly as if he suspected that she had not taken her eyes off him. A shrill whistle floated on the crisp air; Fiona, recognising the tune, smiled wryly as she turned away towards the car. It was 'The Lass of Richmond Hill'. About as inappropriate to the occasion as any tune could be, she decided, as she slid into the car and turned the ignition on. Slowly, carefully, she backed the car around and set off down the road towards the homestead.

CHAPTER FIVE

SHE walked into an uproar. From the kitchen came Jinny's voice raised in anger, the first time she had lost her temper since Fiona had come to Whangatapu, as far as she knew. Fiona was just about to climb the stairs and leave her to it when Jonathan's treble tones came through the closed door, thick with barely hidden fear. All hesitation firmly put behind her, Fiona walked into the kitchen.

The sound of the door opening seemed to freeze those inside the kitchen into a tableau. Jinny, tall and gaunt, her face flushed unbecomingly, Jonathan facing her, his lips trembling but defiance sparkling in his eyes, and, for once at a loss, Ailsa, completely dismayed.

Jonathan broke the spell. He choked out 'Mummy!' and cast himself against Fiona's legs, clinging to her with an abandon that spoke volumes.

'Hey, what's going on?' Fiona said, purposely making her tones light.

'I'll tell you what's going on.' Jinny had regained some control, but her colour was still high and there was open dislike in her expression as she spoke. 'Your son has been rude and defiant, and must be punished.'

'He certainly shall be, if he's been rude or defiant,' Fiona returned calmly. 'Well, Jonathan, how about telling me what happened?'

Manfully holding back his tears, Jonathan looked up at her. 'She said you were no use to anyone,' he muttered. 'If I was rude, so was she. You *are* useful——'

'That will do, love.' One look at the housekeeper's face revealed that he had spoken the truth. There was a certain amount of shame there under the righteous indignation. Fiona bit back a sigh, realising just why Ailsa had lost her usual poise. It was going to take very delicate handling to save face for both Jinny and Jonathan.

'You know, Jonathan, sometimes you hear things that aren't meant for you. I'm quite sure this was one of those things. A gentleman is never rude to a lady, however angry he gets with her, so you must apologise to Jinny. You've made her unhappy, now you must try to make her happy again.'

For a moment she thought she had failed. Jonathan cast Jinny a mutinous look, then heaved a great sigh and relaxed. With adult courtesy he walked across the polished tiles and held out his hand. 'I'm sorry if I was rude,' he said quietly.

For a moment Jinny stared at him, then a great wave of colour suffused her face and neck. Bending down, she took his small hand in hers and said, 'And I'm sorry too, because I was rude to you. I forgot you're nearly a man now.'

Jonathan looked solemnly up at her. 'I are, aren't I?' He removed his hand from hers, and gave her a sudden kiss on the cheek. 'Was Daddy rude to you when he was little?' he asked.

Jinny flushed again, this time with pleasure, and stood up. 'Not very often, and when he was I smacked him with the wooden spoon if he didn't say he was sorry.' Her rare moment of tenderness over she spoke briskly, as though ashamed of it. 'Would you go outside and get me three lemons off the tree in the back garden? I'll make you a lemon pudding for your dinner.'

Gone was the little adult as with a wild whoop he shot out of the door and down the hall, for there was nothing he loved more than lemon pudding, and Jinny could not make it often enough to please him.

Fiona turned to go, aware of Ailsa's relaxation beside her, glad that it had turned out so well. Jinny had learned a lesson, and so, perhaps, had Jonathan.

But the housekeeper stopped her, holding out an awkward hand to lay it on Fiona's arm.

'I'm sorry,' she said with difficulty, after a moment, 'for what I said, too. I had no right . . .'

Fiona might not like her overmuch, but she could not bear to see her humiliated. With the smile that came so rarely she said, 'Not in front of Jonathan, but you have a perfect right to your opinions. Please don't worry about it. I shan't.'

Jinny, however, was determined to do the thing thoroughly. 'No, I can't let it go like that. I am sorry for what I said. I didn't really mean it even when I said it. I was going flat stick and I was angry because things were getting on top of me. Then Tom came in and got in my way, and I asked him why he didn't do something to help, instead of hindering me. He wanted to know why I didn't ask you to do something and I said—what I said. I'm sorry.'

Touched by her sincerity and this first sign of a thaw in the dour housekeeper's attitude, Fiona said gently, 'It's perfectly all right, but thank you for explaining. I know what it's like to have the world fall in on you.' She grinned, the mischief very apparent. 'I notice Tom scarpered while the going was good. Men!'

Ailsa laughed, and after a moment Jinny's expression relaxed into a smile. 'Yes, men! They come and drive you mad with their questions, then disapear when you get mad at them. Well, talking won't get the lunch ready. Artist or no artist, Mr Thurston eats a good substantial meal, and so does his lady wife, for all that she talks of slimming.'

Fiona opened her mouth to offer her help, but Ailsa said swiftly, 'Then we'll go and leave you to it, Jinny dear. Fiona, I hate to tell you, but I've rewritten that last chapter—I saw an absoluely huge loophole you could have driven a bulldozer through and I had to do the whole thing all over again. I was up half the night . . .'

By this time they were outside the kitchen and halfway up the stairs; Mrs Sutherland stopped talking to cast a look around.

'Fiona,' she said, 'that was very well done. Thank you,

my dear. You've breached Jinny's defences now, and it won't be long before she forgets that she ever disliked you. She'll probably try to make amends by asking you to help her with a few things around the house, but whatever you do, *don't* offer! She takes it as an indication that her work is slipping.'

Fiona laughed. 'Then thank you for saving me from blotting my copybook again.'

Apparently her mother-in-law felt the need to explain Jinny's attitude, for she said worriedly, 'She's always been very prickly, but I really do feel that she would die for any of us if the occasion warranted it. And she's extremely fond of Jonathan; she was so angry with him because she was furious with herself for being indiscreet. I think—I suppose she didn't realise he would understand—or care, if it comes to that. He's such an independent child that one tends to assume the bonds between you are not very strong. Well, Jinny knows better now.'

She chuckled reminiscently. 'You should have seen him, Fiona! Just like St George confronting a very nasty dragon! It really gave me a jolt, one I'm not likely to forget. And Jinny certainly won't; only I have a feeling that her respect for you will not be on the surface from now on. You saved her face very effectively.'

Once back in her own bedroom Fiona sat down with a heartfelt sigh on the side of the bed and surveyed her toes with deep abstraction. The incident downstairs had temporarily banished Danny and his ramblings from her mind, but now they came flooding back. Whatever the truth, there had been no mistaking Danny's sincerity, or his deep and abiding bitterness. He certainly believed what he had told Fiona. Did he hold to his beliefs because of anything his sister had told him, or had his mind put two and two together to come up with a not necessarily correct four?

Deliberately calm, she got up and began to tidy up the already tidy room, her normally sensitive mouth compressed into a thin line. She must not think of it until Logan had had a chance to vindicate himself.

He came up half an hour before the lunch gong was due to go and found her seated at the small fruitwood desk, writing a letter to Mrs Wilson in Wellington. Fiona turned to greet him, and saw that he was angry. It did not need a loving wife to guess the meaning of those straight black brows or that twist to his lips. When he was angry his face seemed to settle into a mask, teak-dark, determined and more than a little cruel.

Without preamble he demanded, 'What did Danny Harmon tell you up on the hill this morning?'

'I think you know,' Fiona said quietly.

He glowered down at her, then crossed the room in three strides to stand before her. 'That Mary and I were lovers?'

She nodded, head averted from the searing intensity of his gaze.

'And you believed him.'

It was a statement, not a question. Fiona shook her head. 'I'm not so stupid that I don't know when a man hates and want to hurt. But *he* believes it, Logan. Why?'

'Are you telling me that you don't?' He sounded incredulous, though the hard note of steel was still in his voice, and the hand that caught her chin to turn her face towards him was ungentle.

She met his fierce gaze serenely.

'No, I don't believe him, Logan. You're just not the type.'

He stared at her, then laughed softly in his throat and hauled her up into his arms, holding her fiercely against him, his chin against the top of her head. Every nerve in her body sprang into sentient life, but she resisted their clamour with all of her strength even as her heart beat a suffocating tattoo in her breast.

'You continually surprise me,' he said thickly. 'Why, Fiona?'

'I told you; you're just not the type to get rid of an

inconvenience like that. Why does Danny believe it, Logan?'

'God knows.' He spoke with sombre detachment. 'I don't pretend to be able to fathom out all the workings of Danny's mind; a psychiatrist would probably be able to tell you why it's necessary for him to believe that I seduced Mary. I can't. I thought you would believe him.'

'Is that why you didn't tell me?'

He shrugged, putting her away from him with reluctance. 'I don't know—yes, I suppose so. If I'd told you you might have thought I was just getting in first with an acceptable story.' Frowning, he ran a hand across the back of his neck, arching his back like a man relieved of a burden. Muscles rippled beneath the blue denim, emphasising the vigorous male attraction that accelerated Fiona's pulses every time she was in the same room with her.

Hastily, to hide the physical effect he had on her, she said, 'Logan, he's dangerous. Have you tried reasoning with him?'

He lifted a brow at her, mocking her concern. 'Why the sudden worry? I told you he was unstable, remember, but as you can see that for yourself there's no need to get in a tizz about him. He can't harm you in any way now that you have his measure. Oh, he'll try, but his particular brand of poison can't affect you or Jonathan in any way. As for me'— he grinned, devilishly arrogant and confident—'don't you think I can manage him?'

'Oh, yes,' she retorted, snapping because his self-asurance irritated her even as she responded to it, 'I'm quite sure you could handle anything you set your mind to.'

He watched, smiling with amused mockery as she walked across to twitch the curtain unnecessarily back. His voice followed her, slyly seductive. 'Except for a slip of a girl I should handle with ease. My wife, no less. Where did you get that iron will from, Fiona? You look so fragile, and yet beneath that pale and lovely mask you present to us all, you have the strength of steel.'

With taut lightness, her face averted from him, she

answered coolly, 'Perhaps I'm trying to intrigue you.'

He laughed then, as he walked across to the door into the bathroom. 'No, you have no tricks, darling. None at all.' Over his shoulder he finished mockingly, 'That's why I've given you your head. You don't want any closer relationship just yet, for reasons I can understand even if I don't agree with them. It's pride, I gather, the desire to be considered a person in your own right. It won't be long before that's an accepted fact. When it is, Fiona, nothing you can say or do will prevent me from making this mockery of a marriage into a real one.'

There was a short silence, during which she stood rigidly looking out into the beauty of the garden below, without seeing a single blossom or leaf.

Then he said quite softly, 'And if it's pride that's keeping you silent, don't worry. You've kept it intact by making none of the running, as you said you wouldn't. You won't even have to agree to sharing my bed; when I think the time is ripe I'll save your pride by giving you no choice.'

The threat was underlined by his laughter, drowned a moment later by the sound of water running into the handbasin.

For a long moment Fiona stood like a statue of stone. Then deliberately she forced herself to relax before walking across to the dressing table to pick up her hairbrush.

The rhythmical strokes gave her a measure of calm, outwardly at least; only she knew that deep within her was a tight knot of fear and—yes, she had to admit it to herself, mixed with it was excitement and anticipation. Dear God, was she so frail that she could find pleasure in the thought of submission when every intuitive faculty she possessed was shrieking the wrongness of what he planned? It seemed so, for her colour was high, and deep within the cool grey of her eyes was the sleek contentment of a woman who knows that she is desired—and who desires.

If only she could give in to that half of her which played the traitor, urging her to surrender to her longing for the sensual pleasures she would find in Logan's arms.

But if her body and heart pulled her one way, her brain rejected their soft persuasions. Tightening her lips in a grimace of self-disgust, Fiona pinned back the copper-red waves on either side of her face with two silver bars. Only when it was proved forcibly to her that she could not win Logan's love would she accept second best, and then with a breaking heart. Deluded by his almost impersonal behaviour recently, she had thought that she could prevent the consummation of their marriage if she did not gain his love; now after his last words, she had to face the fact that his purpose was just as strong as ever.

But then, she thought sadly, he would not be the man she loved if he allowed himself to be swayed by anyone's will but his own. And she could not fight for ever that fifth column within her which longed for his strength and his passion, the fulfilment of all the strong attraction that sparked between them. It would be so easy to have the decision taken from her, to find excuses for her weakness. And she must not do it—until it was forced upon her by the knowledge that she had failed in her effort to win his love.

At Whangatapu the mail came after lunch. It was dropped off at a box at the top of the hill by the mailman, who signified its arrival by a prolonged blast on the horn of his van. Tom usually went up to get it and after dropping off the homestead's lot went on to make the delivery at the other houses. With the mail came the newspapers and any articles the families might have ordered from the village by telephone, for the rural delivery van delivered almost anything.

So after lunch in every house on the station one could be almost certain that there was a period of quiet relaxation as everyone read the newspapers and what letters they had received.

Ailsa broke this silence by muttering something under her breath in such agitation that Fiona looked up from her book. Frowning deeply, Ailsa peered into the leaves of the diary which was never far from her.

'Bother!' she said frustratedly. 'Oh, *bother*! Really—this is too much! Logan!'

He raised his brows. 'What is it?'

'Do you remember my telling you about a garden club from Auckland which is doing a kind of horticultural tour of the north? They want to spend an hour or so here, because it's one of the few examples of a Colonial garden left. Well, this is a letter from the secretary. She hopes I don't mind, but they've put the tour forward and they'll be here on Friday.'

'Does it matter what day they'll be here?'

'No, I suppose not, but I do like to know where I am. I'll have to ring up Marie Ramsey and tell her to organise our Garden Circle; we're giving them afternoon tea. And I must get Tom on to the lawns. I thought we had another ten days before they came; the Judas tree would have been in full flower then.'

Mrs Thurston set her book aside. 'The garden looks lovely, Ailsa, and it couldn't be more immaculate, so don't get upset; although I must say it's inconsiderate of them to leave it till this late date to let you know. We can all help with anything that needs doing.'

'That's sweet of you, thank you.' Ailsa cast a hurried glance at the letter in her hand. 'The afternoon tea we can leave to Jinny and the Garden Circle. I must make a list of things to be done before they come. Come on, Fiona, we'll go and do it now.'

Fiona rose to her feet obediently, but as she made to follow Mrs Sutherland out of the door Logan folded the newspaper and set it down, saying abruptly, 'You'll have to do without Fiona for a few minutes, Mother. I want to talk to her.'

Astonishment lifted his mother's brows momentarily, but she was in too much of a hurry to demur, so Fiona meekly allowed herself to be escorted out of the drawing room and into the study.

Logan stopped by the desk and said brusquely, 'Why do you let her order you around as if you were her employee?'

Sheer bewilderment robbed Fiona of speech. She swallowed, then said quietly, 'That's just her manner. You should know that, Logan.'

'She does it because you allow her to. And I don't like it. If you would make some effort she would be more than glad to hand over the reins to you. My mother has never been particularly domesticated, but you are my wife, Fiona! I will not have people discussing my marriage, wondering why you make no attempt to assert yourself, as I saw the Thurstons doing just then. God knows, there's been enough gossip.'

His sharp, brusque tones angered her. Without stopping to think she flashed back, 'I'm not needed as a hostess here! This place runs so well that my presence is quite unnecessary, especially as you have a very charming substitute in Denise Page.'

A moment's silence, fraught with tension, then he said tightly, 'So you're jealous of her. I thought as much. Why? Because she has poise and the ability to make others feel welcome? All attributes you lack, Fiona, and apparently have no intention of acquiring.'

He drew a breath, cast a glittering glance of dislike at her and went on with hard decision, 'Well, you can damned well start thinking of other people besides your own precious self. Whangatapu has always had a reputation for hospitality, one which is dear to us. You are not going to destroy that reputation. As it seems that the only way to make you feel as though you belong here is to make it a concrete fact, I'll tell Jinny and my mother that from now on you'll run the house completely.'

His anger and contempt seared her, but she could not allow herself to dwell on her own feelings; her spiteful remark about Denise Page had already brought a reaction which showed her how insubstantial were the hopes she had felt a short hour ago of making him love her.

With gritty persistence she stated, 'If you do that you'll

destroy any chance I ever had of being what you want me to be. I have no experience of running a place like this—I wouldn't know how to go about it. And if you force your mother—and especially Jinny—to accept me as an imposition, they'll hate me, and I won't blame them in the least.'

'Then you'll just have to put up with their hatred,' he said coldly. 'And don't over-dramatise. Neither of them is prone to attacks of emotionalism, so although they may be a little surprised at my decision, they won't think it strange. They'll both be considerably more surprised if I allow this situation to continue. My wife is not a nonentity, and I refuse to allow you to behave as one. You're jealous of Denise only because you see in her the things you should be. Once your position in the house is made quite clear you'll have no cause to be so envious of her; you may find that she's an extremely pleasant girl, and a good friend.'

His words were like stones, hitting her with such precision that it occurred to her that he was aiming them directly. Was this his way of telling her that she was living in a mist of illusions? Whatever he felt for Denise was powerful enough to cause this cold anger over a few malicious words disparaging her.

Calling her pride to her aid, she said equally coldly, 'Very well then, if that's the way you want it.'

'I do. I'm prepared to wait a little longer, as I told you before lunch, for you to accept that I have rights to your person, but you can start earning your keep in other ways. Jonathan no longer needs your constant attendance, so you can't make him your excuse for not wanting responsibility.'

Through pale lips she said fiercely, 'You have a delightful turn of phrase, Logan. I understand you perfectly. Value for money expended, is that what you want? Very well, you shall have it. I hope it satisfies you!'

She cast him one scorching glance, then slipped out of the room, sick and trembling at the memories which that closed, ruthless countenance brought back. That was exactly how he had looked after the night they spent together, the night Jonathan was conceived, and she could not take any more of his brutality. Without volition she walked into the kitchen.

'What on——' Jinny dropped the tea-towel in her agitation. 'Here, sit down. I'll get you a drink of water.'

The liquid was cool on her tongue, dispelling the nausea. Fiona drank it off, then pushed a trembling hand through her hair, undoing the wide silver clasps to free it, for it dragged unbearably at her temples.

'I'm sorry,' she said after a moment, 'I've just had the father and mother of a row with Logan.'

As soon as the words came she regretted them, but Jinny merely sniffed.

'No man would ever get me in that state,' she retorted tartly, washing the glass out. 'I'm not surprised, mind you, I've seen it coming. You should have too.'

Fiona leant forward, resting her arms on the cool, satin-smooth kauri table, white with continual scrubbing. 'I don't know him all that well.'

'No, and he doesn't know you either. Well, what's to do?'

'He says I've got to take over the running of the house.' There, it was out, bald and unvarnished with smooth words.

Another sniff from the housekeeper. 'Well, why all the tragedy? You can do it. Mrs Sutherland will be happy enough to hand over, and I won't say I couldn't do with a bit of help.'

'Oh, it's hopeless,' Fiona returned drearily. 'Not that part of it—if you'll show me I can manage that. But I have to be the lady of the house—*the* Mrs Sutherland. And she'll never understand.'

'Good lord, you don't see much, do you!' Jinny's voice was irritated as she rattled cups and put the electric jug on. 'She's been wondering ever since you came why you tucked yourself in the background so very definitely and refused to be lured out.' She took down the tea caddy, measured the tea into the teapot, and poured in the boiling water. 'It's about time you and I had a bit of a talk, I'm thinking. Now, drink that cup of tea up and listen.'

But she was silent for some moments, obviously marshalling her thoughts. Fiona sipped the tea, grateful for the New Zealand custom which stipulated tea to be the remedy for all ills, mental and bodily, that afflicted mankind.

'I don't quite know how to begin,' Jinny stated, her shrewd eyes watchful above the steam from her cup, 'but I don't suppose I can do worse by leaping straight in. You've had a roughish sort of a spin here, mainly because we all thought that Logan and Denise Page would get married, and we liked the idea. She's all that a Sutherland should be, beautiful, charming, an accomplished hostess, an organiser who could take Mrs Sutherland's place in the district affairs. It's an important place. Over the years people around here have got into the habit of looking up to the Sutherlands, expecting them to act as the motivating force whenever one is needed. And Denise would be ideal. She's popular and knows everyone. O.K., I was happy because I knew, like Mrs Sutherland, that things would be much the same. Denise wouldn't interfere with me and my ways. Then you came along.'

She sipped her tea, scrutinising the downcast face opposite her with something like anger. 'Well, you can't blame us for being suspicious. We didn't know what sort of person you would be. But we decided to make the best of things, for Jonathan and for Logan. When you arrived you were totally different from what we expected. Physically, you'd do. You have the beauty, you speak well, your manners are excellent. But that's all. Denise shows you up whenever she's here, and you don't seem to care. You're obviously not in love with Logan. In almost every respect you're as minus as Denise is plus. Well, I don't know how you react when you meet someone who's just going through the motions, but it makes me angry. I love Logan as much as I love my own son, and I couldn't help feeling he'd got the thin end of the stick.'

She shrugged, her thick black brows meeting across her nose. 'You weren't shy, so it wasn't that. If you had been we'd have done our best to get you out of it. You just seemed—disinterested. So we were disinterested too. Now I'm not interested in your personal affairs—at least I am, for Logan's sake, but it's none of my business—but it's about time that you started to behave like his wife, instead of moping around the place. It won't be long before we start having summer visitors, and they're going to carry stories about you back to Auckland, and those people are Logan's friends too. You owe it to him not to give them any cause to gossip about him.'

'I'm sick of that word,' Fiona said sharply. 'I owe to everyone. Nobody owes anything to me!'

'Stop pitying yourself. If you wanted an easy life you shouldn't have got tangled up with the Sutherlands!'

Reluctantly Fiona smiled. Jinny's down-to-earth appraisal of the situation had by some mysterious method restored her faith in herself, a faith which had taken a battering in the last few weeks. 'I didn't get tangled up with them,' she retorted, 'I got snatched into orbit.'

'Well, you'll have to make the best of it. Materially you've got everything you could ever want. Logan's a millionaire, though I'll give you credit for not knowing that. You certainly aren't greedy.'

Astonishment shaped Fiona's mouth into an O of wonderment. 'Is he really? I didn't think there were millionaires in New Zealand. It certainly didn't occur to me that Logan was one.'

'Because he works on the property?' Jinny asked drily. 'You must know his other interests, girl, you've been doing his typing. He doesn't direct companies for nothing. And there are shares and things. I've not much interest in that, but yes, he's a millionaire. Finished your tea?'

'Yes, but I'd like another cup. I'll get it.'

When Fiona was seated again Jinny asked briskly,

'Where is Jonathan?'

'Sleeping. He was tired out, so I put him down to rest.'

'How's he getting on at the Play Centre?'

Fiona's face lit up. 'Marvellously well. He loves it, and he's made friends so easily. His cough has gone just as the doctor promised it would.'

'Good.' Not for worlds would Jinny have admitted how that cough had worried her, but her expression was almost soft as she went on, 'You did the right thing, coming here, you know.'

'It certainly was for Jonathan.'

'It was right for everyone,' Jinny said firmly. 'You'll realise that one day. Now, to work. If you like you can take over the looking after of the place—I mean the dusting and polishing and tidying up. That will give me more time to attend to cooking and washing—that sort of thing, and with the typing you do you'll find your days pretty full. These old houses have to be continually looked after if they're to look nice. I wouldn't say anything to Mrs Sutherland. Just go ahead and do what's needed. She probably won't even notice, for she's not much use in the house really. More the gardening type.'

'Oh! That reminds me.' Swiftly Fiona told her of the projected visit of the Garden Club.

Jinny's expression grew dour. 'With shearing starting in a week's time I don't need a pack of women preparing afternoon tea in my kitchen,' she declared roundly, 'but I suppose I'll have to put up with them. I'll make sponges and freeze them. You wouldn't believe it, most of these Garden Club ladies will be over forty and overweight, but they'll all tuck into sponges filled with whipped cream! Still, Tom will be in his element. Nothing he likes more than showing people around his blessed garden. You'd better pull out all the stops with your flower arrangements. Where will you serve the tea?'

'On the terrace if it's fine,' Fiona said promptly. 'If not—well, it will have to be the drawing-room, I suppose, and hang the Persian carpet!'

'Bits of grass all over it,' Jinny agreed gloomily. 'They won't stay on the paths. Still, there's nothing like a Persian carpet for wear.'

The kitchen door opened enough to allow Jonathan to insinuate himself into the room. Just woken up he bore that rosy, newly hatched look which belied his strong features but was reinforced by his angelic smile.

'I'm awake,' he announced unnecessarily, 'and I'm hungry. May I have an orange, Mummy?'

'Yes, my love. Go and pick yourself one, and I'll peel it.'

He pondered for a moment, then asked, 'Could it be a tangelo? Tom showed me how you squeeze them all over to make them very, very juicy, then you extra carefully take out a little piece of the skin at the stalk end and if Jinny gives me a sugar lump I can suck the juice through it.'

Fiona regarded him for a moment. 'I think Tom is a bad influence on you, my lad. You must ask Jinny for the sugar lump first.'

A nod from Jinny was all that Jonathan needed. He chuckled as he headed out of the door, saying over his shoulder, 'I won't forget my gumboots, 'cause the grass is still a bit dampish, Tom says, and he's just cut it.'

'I can't get over the likeness,' Jinny said absently. 'That touch of red in his hair and the way he plays the piano is all he got from you. Although that's not quite true. I can't put my finger on it, but there's a difference between him and what Logan was like at the same age. Logan was as tough as they came. He had to be—his father was the old school, a proper Victorian. Jonathan seems to be more—more sensitive, I suppose, though there's no weakness there. He's got the same lordly manner, but he—oh, I don't know,' she abandoned psychology for something much more congenial.

'We'd better start talking about this party. Dinner with the Pages before, and then about fifty people, Mrs Sutherland said, so that will mean snacks all through the evening and a buffet round about midnight. Logan will attend to the drinks, so we don't have to worry about that. Any ideas?'

'Not immediately, and probably not ever,' Fiona smiled. 'Not my style of entertaining, but I'll give it some thought.' Her eyes became abstracted, almost gloomy, as the sensitive mouth hardened.

'Nervous?'

She looked up, saw understanding in the housekeeper's expression and nodded. 'Yes, but I'll cope. I didn't realise that Logan was—well, so important. We lived a fairly retired life, my parents and I. Dad was a schoolteacher, Mum stayed at home. Dad loved his job and the area where we lived, so he never tried for promotion. I didn't know there were people who lived like this. I suppose I feel a bit—well, inferior. Except that it's not that.'

She glanced helplessly round the sparkling kitchen, fitted with every conceivable labour-saving device. 'The whole set-up is totally foreign to my conception of how New Zealanders live. And yet all of the people I've met take it for granted. They've grown up in conditions of luxury, and it shows in the sophisticated way they talk and act. At times I feel like a foreigner.'

'They're all human,' Jinny returned drily, 'even that handsome brute you've got for a husband, and they all have the usual needs and desires and failings. Think of them like that, and you won't be quite so self-conscious. What are you going to wear to this do?'

Fiona chuckled, remembering her fury at her mother-in-law's tactlessness. 'Something that will set them back on their heels,' she said mysteriously. 'Even that handsome brute of a husband of mine will have his eyes opened!'

'I hope you're prepared to take the consequences,' Jinny said in tones of marked disapproval. 'Logan's got a fairly strict idea on what's due to his position. That's his father coming out in him. He was a proper martinet, but he was a good boss, very fair and just. Logan's more human, for all that he's as tough.'

Fiona laughed as she stood up. 'I shan't wear anything outrageous, I promise you. And I shall be on my best behaviour—for your sake, Jinny.'

'Do it for Logan's sake—or better still, for your own.' The tone was crisp, but there was a lurking softness in Jinny's expression which would have surprised any other member of the household had they seen it.

CHAPTER SIX

THE new understanding between them made a difference to Fiona. At least, she thought in the days that followed, there was one member of the household who didn't whole-heartedly disapprove of her. It amazed her that it should be Jinny who had thawed, for after that first cold, watchful look from the housekeeper on the day she arrived at Whangatapu she had been convinced that the most she could hope for from Jinny was tolerance. But now, even if only for Logan's sake, there was active help for her, and Jinny's dry, caustic tongue to set many of her problems in perspective.

Except the biggest one. Logan had retreated behind a wall of icy indifference in private, and cool but possessive courtesy when there were others present. The Thurstons were still with them in the mornings and evenings; during the day they made long expeditions when both sketched. Fiona found herself drawn to them, for there were no hidden currents in her commerce with them, and it seemed that only with them could she fully relax. With Jinny there was always the knowledge that in taking Fiona in hand she had the continued welfare and prestige of the Sutherlands at heart. The Thurstons, although they must have heard the story of the hasty marriage and her subsequent flight, never betrayed by a word or look that they found her presence at the homestead a subject of interest.

The evening before the Garden Club's visit was fine, mild enough to be called summery. The french doors were left open after dusk, and they had drinks out there until the heavy fall of dew drove them inside just as Venus rose, a brazenly gold disc against the green twilight sky.

'It seems close enough to pick, doesn't it,' Mrs Thurston commented idly. 'I love these northern twilights. They're so short that one can miss them if one is inside, and yet there's an atmosphere like no other. Smell those freesias! Heavenly.'

There was a companionable silence, before her husband said, 'Play something appropriate, Fiona. I feel a pleasantly gentle melancholy stealing over me, and I want to indulge it.'

Fiona smiled, rose, and went in through the open doors into the music room. They were left open for much of the time now, to make it easier for her to play.

For a few moments she flirted with the keyboard before her fingers slid into place and she played a simple tune, old, hauntingly wistful, singing the air as she played. Her voice was clear and true, without affectation or training yet ideally capturing the sad resignation of the song.

'I know the words, of course,' Forrest said quietly when she had finished. 'John, Earl of Bristol, wrote it three hundred years ago, if I remember correctly.

"Grieve not, dear love! although we often part,
But know that Nature doth us gently sever
Thereby to train us up with tender art
To brook the day when we must part forever.
For Nature, doubting we should be surprised
By that sad day whose dred doth chiefly fear us,
Doth keep us daily schooled and exercised
Lest that the fright thereof should overbear us!"

Thank you, Fiona. Now, something a little more cheerful, less touched with old, far-off emotions.'

She laughed and played from *Carnival of the Animals* a witty sophisticated frothy piece that drove away any lingering drifts of melancholy that her first choice might have given rise to.

'You *are* good,' Ailsa commented idly. 'I wonder if Tom remembered to pick up that pile of prunings by the rock roses. I have the horrible feeling that there's one thing I've forgotten to do.'

'Relax, Ailsa.' Thurston set his sherry glass down as

though he had finally made a momentous decision. A look passed between him and his wife. When he received an almost imperceptible nod from her he turned to Logan, dark against the curtains, and said, 'I'd like to paint your wife, Logan. Any objections?'

Fiona; astounded, looked from one to the other. Forrest was almost diffident; from where she sat she could hardly see Logan's face, for the lights had not been turned on, but she felt the dagger-sharp glance he sent her and averted her head, half afraid that he might choose to jeer at the artist's choice.

Instead he returned mildly, 'Not yet, Forrest. She hasn't matured enough for your brush.'

Disappointment gleamed in the artist's narrow eyes, but he said, 'Perhaps not, although it's that air of innocence I'd like to capture before it goes. A year with you, Logan, and she'll have lost it for good.'

Logan smiled, a flash of white in the dimness as he observed lightly, 'I'll take that as a compliment, even though I'm damned sure it's not meant as one. Whoever heard of the mother of a four-year-old son being innocent?'

'There's an inward innocence that never fades,' Mrs Thurston commented in her brisk, homely tones, easing the tension which seemed to have sprung up from nowhere. 'Was that a native pigeon I saw in the jacaranda? I didn't think there were many of them left.'

'We get one quite often.' Fiona backed her up, walking across to stand in the opening. 'Yes, it's him—and oh, look, he has a mate with him!'

From behind came Logan's voice, a subtle mockery in the words. 'Naturally. It's spring, mating time. Hadn't you noticed, Fiona?'

Something thickened in her throat, making her voice almost husky as she laughed. 'Living on a farm, how could I help but notice? Yesterday Jonathan told me the facts of life!'

There was laughter, muted but appreciative, and over it Ailsa's voice. 'And that, I think, is one of the advantages of living on a farm—a much more practical attitude to sex among the children. Which reminds me, Logan. Denise rang up today and said that Jody has whelped and would you like to go over and choose the pup you want. Apparently she's giving Jonathan one, although I think a farm dog would have been much more sensible. What on earth are we going to do with a fox terrier?'

'It's not what we do with it, it's what Jonathan will do,' Logan said coolly, moving forward to cut Fiona off from the rest of the room. Half turning, she cast him one sparkling glance of dislike, then allowed herself to be led out on to the terrace. Logan made some joke over his shoulder that brought an appreciative chuckle from those still inside, then took her elbow to lead her firmly down the steps and out across the grass towards the bottom of the garden. As they reached the dark shadows of the shelter belt he queried on a jeer, 'Disappointed?'

'About what?' Fiona asked grittily.

'Because I won't let our resident artist immortalise your lovely face.'

Shrugging, she retorted, 'No. I didn't know he wanted to.'

'I've seen that glint in his eye before, so I was forewarned. He knew I wouldn't allow it, of course, but you can't blame a man for trying.'

The casuarinas smelt spicy in the damp air, pleasantly astringent against the more exotic perfumes of the spring flowers. Fiona put up a hand to capture a feathery twig, determined not to ask him why he had refused Forrest's request, yet reluctant to annoy him by staying silent.

'No, I don't,' she murmured. Their feet brushed against the low mound of lemon-scented thyme between the flagstones, releasing the delicious fragrance.

'Not at all curious?' he asked, mockery very evident in his tone of voice.

'About what?' She was deliberately obtuse.

One hand tugged a strand of hair so sharply that it brought tears to her eyes. 'Don't play games, my love.' His fingers threaded through the silken strands, pulling her to a stop against him.

She waited docilely in his grasp, pulses leaping at his closeness. Anger was palpable in his fingers, in the tautness of his voice as he said quietly, 'No other man is going to have from you what you deny me. I mean your time, your attention, your confidence. He sees too much, and he would have your soul laid bare on that canvas of his, and your soul, my darling, as well as your body, belongs to me, not to anyone who cares to look at a painting of you.'

Striving to keep her voice steady, she asked, 'Did you bring me out to tell me that? Because if you did, the dew is heavy and——'

Fingers tightened cruelly in her hair, jerking her head back against his arm. She stared up into what should have been the darkness of his face, but a faint light revealed his features, forbidding and ruthless against the soft whiteness of the jasmine.

'The light of Venus,' he said softly, meaningly. 'It's very rare that Venus casts enough light to see by. Perhaps it's an omen.'

The kiss was savage, as if he was purging himself of his anger and frustration by bruising her lips, but after a few moments the quality of it changed, and he muttered something against her mouth before kissing the cool skin of her throat, pressing a necklace around the fine bones of her shoulders. A warm golden tide of emotion began to cloud Fiona's thinking; without volition she sighed and relaxed against him. Her hands crept up to clasp his head, pulling it down when he would have raised it.

'Fiona——' he muttered thickly, his hands heavy against her hips, 'darling——'

She opened her mouth to whisper something to him, then was lost in a rocketing blaze of sensation as he plundered the sweetness she had inadvertently surrendered.

Long moments later he released her, smiling down into the bemused oval of her face, his breath coming heavily.

'Call that a reward for good behaviour,' he said unpleasantly. 'I've noticed your work around the house.'

Reaction stiffened her back. Unconsciously squaring her shoulders, she retorted, 'Well, you said you wanted value for money. I hope you're getting it.'

'You said that, not me. You don't know what I want of you even though you think you have it all mapped out. I never doubted your prowess in the housewifely arts. Now all you have to do is show a comparable improvement as a hostess. I'll be watching you tomorrow and over the weekend. Two days with my sullen brother and his scatty wife should show me just how well you shape up. They daunt even Mother!'

Fiona moved away from him to look intently out to sea, one slender hand crushing a spray of jasmine. The scent floated thickly around them, romantically pervasive on the cool crisp air.

'Logan, why did you marry me?' she asked quietly. 'You must have known I would be out of place here. I had no idea what this place was like, but you knew.'

'Inverted snobbery?' he sounded amused, totally master of any situation. 'You know why I married you. I wanted Jonathan. As for the other—you must suffer from a whacking great inferiority complex if you really think you can't cope with a situation like this. Whangatapu is no different from hundreds of other stations up and down the country, except that it's larger than most. Any woman who managed single-handedly to bring up a child on the allowance that the Government grants to solo parents needn't be worried about running a place like this, especially when you have Jinny to help you.'

'I had my parents for the first two years,' she murmured. 'I don't think I would have been able to manage without their support.'

'Support that I should have given you,' he said coldly. 'Did you ever think of adopting him out?'

She turned to him, emotion giving her expression a fierce determination. 'No. Never. He was—he was mine. I couldn't. It was selfish, perhaps—he might have been better off in a family.'

'I wondered. Well, as it happens, it was for the best. He gained you a husband, and security. Those are supposed to be a woman's greatest needs, aren't they?'

The taunt made her flush angrily, but she shrugged with assumed indifference, returning, 'So they say. Certainly most women seem to need them.'

'Except Fiona Sutherland, who managed quite adequately for two years without either.' He smiled, and took her arm. 'Look, the moon is coming up. Much as I'd like to dally with you I think we'd better go back. It must be nearly dinner time——'

'—and Jinny hates to be kept waiting,' she finished pertly. '*Lay on, Macduff.*'

He laughed, and to those who waited in the big drawing-room it seemed that all was well between them. Only Forrest Thurston looked keenly at them as they came in through the french doors, his dark eyes keen and sharp as they rested on Fiona's mouth, reddened by Logan's kisses, and from that moved to the narrowed arrogance of her husband's smile. And what he thought no one knew.

By half-past three Fiona was rag-tired but buoyed up by an intense satisfaction that lent a sparkle to her eyes and a warm smile to her lips. The Garden Club ladies were happy, Tom and Ailsa were happy, even Jinny permitted a relaxation of her features which must denote some sort of pleasure.

The beauty and brilliance of the day had started it, for it turned out to be one of those gold and blue spring days when the wind slept and the sea sparkled and the new growth in the paddock lay emerald and lime under the sun. Bees drifted somnolently around the garden, plundering sweetness from every available bloom. Those bees, or a swarm of their restless sisters, had almost caused a crisis a bare hour before the large silver and blue coach pulled up outside the front door, for they had left their hive in the orchard and settled in a buzzing determined heap on one of the wooden columns which supported the portico.

But Tom came to the rescue, watched wide-eyed by Jonathan and Fiona as he had coaxed the swarm into a new hive. Now they were re-settled under the cerise pink drift of a peach tree in the farthest reaches of the orchard.

Tom dropped his veil and gloves and appeared in his best clothes, ready to show the visitors around his beloved garden. The ladies from the local Gardening Circle, having parked their cars discreetly in the big gravel area by the implement shed, had tripped in with their covered plates and dishes bearing their contributions to the afternoon tea, and had set it out on tables on the terrace, covering everything with embroidered nylon showers to keep insects off. Now they were busy making tea and setting out the cups.

Even the bus driver was happy. He must have been chosen for his interest in gardening, for he was inspecting with the eyes of a connoisseur the camellia trees, whistling tunelessly through his teeth as he did so, his peaked cap pushed far back on his bald head.

And certainly, when it was time, the women from Auckland tucked in with a will, demolishing Jinny's sponges and other frivolous cakes as well as the more pedestrian sandwiches and gingerbread. Fiona moved quietly among them, smiling, talking, listening to the conversation, refilling cups and passing plates. She had expected to feel ill at ease, but everyone was determined to please and be pleased, and she found herself responding to the atmosphere without any diffidence at all.

Then the President made a short speech thanking them, presented Ailsa with a beautiful book on English gardens, and they were gone, leaving behind them that empty, let-down feeling which always attacks when visitors have gone and there is a lot of cleaning up to do.

Fiona looked across the terrace to her mother-in-law, saw her put a hand to her brow with a grimace, hastily erased, and made her way across to her.

'Have you a headache?' she asked softly.

'Oh dear, was it that obvious?'

'No, I'm sure I was the only one to notice. Why don't you go and lie down? Jinny and I can cope here.'

Ailsa wavered, then capitulated. 'My dear, I shall—and thank you. I haven't said anything, but you've taken a lot of the work off my shoulders and I'm grateful. Where is Jonathan?'

'Out with Logan, drafting sheep. I'll see that he doesn't disturb you when he comes in.'

'I'll be fine after half an hour or so, so don't worry.'

There followed a cheerful half-hour that was not without strain for Fiona. Most of the women who helped wash and dry the dishes and clear up were friendly, but she could feel their curiosity and once, when one of them mentioned Denise, there were several covert looks to see how she took the reference. Inwardly shrinking, she replied in a pleasant matter-of-fact voice, which she hoped would allay any wild flights of gossip, but it was with relief that she waved the last car and its occupant goodbye and turned back to the house.

The back garden was Jinny's domain, a kind of glorified herb garden-cum-vegetable plot where parsley rioted among sage and oregano and chives bordered beds of early lettuces and late cauliflowers. It caught the afternoon sun and was a lazy, peaceful place with a huge old Japanese walnut tree as a centrepiece. Fiona moved a red plastic watering can from an old log of wood and sat down, letting the drowsy peacefulness soak into her soul.

Bees hummed busily on the tiny lilac thyme flowers while one large, clumsy bumble bee plundered a bright orange marigold. A lamb's voice came on the quiet air, to be followed almost immediately by the reassuring bleat of a ewe. The sky was still blue, but an indefinable change in the air told of approaching dusk, and from the green canopy of the walnut came the evening hymn of a thrush, singing as though it would burst. A horse neighed, there was the thud of hooves on soft grass, and Jonathan laughed in the distance.

Fiona smiled. For the first time she felt at home here, part of the routine of life at Whangatapu. In this quiet haven she was at one with the sounds of the place, soothed and yet exhilarated by them. Behind her the big house drowsed, a lovely relic of the past made even more beautiful by its use as a family home. To Jonathan it would be home all his life, if he wished it, for he was a Sutherland, and this place was bred deep in his bones. Whatever career he chose he would always retain his links with Whangatapu, the home of his forebears.

The click of a latch made her look up. They were coming in under the casuarinas, both almost identically clad in blue jeans and short-sleeved cotton shirts, a pullover slung casually over one shoulder. Jonathan was tired, but he walked on sturdily, his gait so like Logan's that it brought a lump to her throat. Logan must have come home like that at the end of a long day, worn out but refusing to give in to his tiredness. And perhaps, if Ailsa ever waited for him under the walnut tree, Logan's face had broken into the same sleepy grin as he saw her.

'Hi, Mummy!' He ran the last few steps, buried his head in her chest, his strong young arms tight around her waist. 'Mm, you smell nice. Daddy and me have been drafting the sheep all afternoon. Did you have a nice time with your ladies?'

'Very nice, thank you.' She buried her face in the hot head, then sneezed as the fine hair tickled her nostrils. 'You smell of horse.'

'I've been riding on Sultan with Daddy.' He pulled away. 'Is there any afternoon tea left over, 'cause I'm starving, and I bet Daddy is too.'

Fiona looked up, laughing, into Logan's face. The laughter died away as she met his eyes, for he was staring down at her with an intentness she had never surprised in his expression before, a kind of piercing scrutiny which stripped her bare of her defences. He looked like one of the cowboys in Jonathan's favourite T.V. shows, lean and broad of shoulder, strikingly handsome against the sky, his male vitality emphasised by the working clothes he wore, and his gaze devouring her.

The peace that had enveloped her fled. Without volition she put her hand out, but he disregarded it, still standing motionless as if he were transfixed. Her hand dropped; colour flooded her cheeks as she said uncertainly, 'Have you had a good day, Logan?'

'Oh, it went off very well.'

She got to her feet, made an unnecessary thing of brushing her skirt, then took Jonathan's hand and fell into step beside Logan. 'Come on, love, I'll get you bathed, then you can have your dinner. And we must be quiet when we're upstairs, because Gran has a headache and is resting.'

'O.K.,' Jonathan said charmingly, before he was seized with an enormous yawn. 'Daddy said I can ride my own horse soon,' he confided after a moment. 'And he said you can learn to ride too, then we can all go together.'

Fiona looked down fondly at him, repressing a shudder at the thought. 'Would you like that?'

'Yes. We could take a picnic ...' He yawned again, then stumbled.

Logan bent, picked him up and carried him into the house, his face blank and cold, a carved mask to hide his thoughts, leaving Fiona to follow behind, her mind a bewildered tangle of wonderment.

When she came down the Thurstons had arrived back, Mrs Thurston mourning a skin that had seen too much of the sun.

'You would think I was too old a hand to get burned,' she grumbled good-humouredly, 'but there's no fool like an old fool. Ailsa not well, Fiona?'

'No, she has a headache, so I've persuaded her to stay in bed.'

'Tension. She gets all worked up and then wham! A good night's sleep is what she needs.'

Fiona nodded. 'Yes, she said that. Hasn't it been a fabulous day?'

Mrs Thurston smiled at the eager young face. 'Yes, it

has, and it's going to be a lovely evening to match. Not that I'll see much of it. Forrest made me walk at least five miles today, and I'm bushed. I'll have an early night, I think.'

'Me too.' Her husband screwed his face up in a comical grimace of pain. 'I've got too soft, and now I'm going to pay for it with stiff muscles.'

True to their intention they retired early, leaving Fiona and Logan alone in the music room. Fiona lay back in her chair, listening raptly to the *Enigma Variations*, her expressive face remote and pale in the subdued lighting. No one could have guessed that she was acutely conscious of Logan reading a great heavy tome opposite her.

When the record finished he looked up, smiling with a warmth she had never expected to see in his eyes. 'You look very pretty, but too far away. Come and join me on the sofa.'

There was no excuse she could make to prevent such perilous intimacy, so she allowed herself to be pulled down beside him. Quickly, to hide her tension, she said, 'What are you reading?'

'Genetics.' He slanted her a sideways smile, mocking her astonishment. 'A working knowledge is helpful when one is breeding stock.'

'But that's all theory.' She looked down at the page, her brows wrinkling as she saw several words of horrifying appearance. 'Goodness, it looks difficult! Do you understand that?' One slender finger pointed to the page.

He laughed, and captured her hand, holding it to his breast before bringing it up to his mouth. Against the palm he said softly, 'Yes, I understand it, but I'll agree that it's dry stuff, and not at all appropriate for the occasion. Do you realise, my lovely wife, that this is the first time in all these weeks we've been alone in the evening together? Your pulse is fluttering like a moth against my thumb. Are you afraid of me, Fiona?'

With difficulty she forced laughter into her voice. 'Yes, when you're like this. You're too good at dalliance, Logan.'

'Signs of a misspent youth.' He turned, pulling her across

his knees. The book thudded unnoticed to the floor, his hand traced the contours of her face, moving lightly, lingeringly across the fine skin with a lover's touch. 'God, but you're beautiful,' he said beneath his breath. 'Why did I choose a wife with ironclad principles? And why do I have to be so stupid as to consider them? I should damned well seduce you tonight, and then we'd have an end to all of this tension.' His hand moved to cover her lips. 'No, don't say anything. Not yet, anyway.'

It was too easy to turn her head into his shoulder, too easy to rejoice at the slow heavy thud of his heartbeat against her cheek. He held her closely, but not too tightly against him, his mouth against her forehead. The record had changed to *Songs of Auvergne*, and as the soprano's sensuous voice thrilled around the room Fiona relaxed into the warmth of his embrace, and the peace she had lost under his gaze that afternoon came back to her like an opiate to a brain already tired, so that when he kissed her she did not resist, even when his mouth and hands became demanding and forceful. As his fingers slid the zip of her dress down she did protest, but he laughed and smothered her words, and after that she did not think, for her passion grew to meet his, and she knew that this sweet ecstasy of body and mind was what she had been born for.

It was the repeated shrilling of the telephone which brought her back to her senses. Logan, too, lifted his head from the scented hollow between her breasts to mutter forcefully, 'Damn!'

But he got up, putting her to one side before he moved across the room to pick up the receiver. Somehow his shirt had become unbuttoned; as she straightened the top of her dress Fiona found her eyes on that expanse of chest, teak-brown and smooth except for the wedge of dark soft hair across it.

'Oh—Denise,' Logan said somewhat abstractedly. 'Yes, what is it?'

Fiona stiffened. Her first thoughts as she pulled the zip up at the back of her dress were chagrined, but before long she was devoutly thankful for the interruption, for Logan's voice became warm and charged with an intimate note which grated unbearably on her ears.

'Yes, yes, I got your message. I've been busy with other things.'

Trying to seduce your wife, thought Fiona bitterly, touching her hair with restless fingers.

He laughed into the receiver. 'No, my child, I haven't forgotten. Oh, you are? Well yes, of course, I'd be delighted to take you with me. I'll be leaving early though, and I warn you, if you're not ready I'll leave you behind ... Stay the night? An excellent idea.' His eyes roved the room, finally coming to rest with speculative mockery on Fiona, now apparently very interested in the record collection. 'No, Fiona won't object. Why should she?'

It was the last taunting question which made Fiona's mouth harden into a thin line. How could he speak so slightingly, when only a few minutes before he had been making violent love to her? It was, she told herself grimly, just as well Denise had rung up, before she suffered the humiliation of surrendering to Logan's lust, only to find that it changed nothing. It seemed that he was still determined to have his cake and eat it too.

He was laughing again, and after a teasing farewell the receiver clicked as it was set back in place. Fiona pulled out a record, staring at the brightly coloured sleeve with eyes which saw nothing.

'You wouldn't like that,' Logan said softly from behind her. 'It's one of Denise's—music to romance by.'

'I hope it served its purpose,' she returned politely, shoving the offensive thing back into the rack with jerky force.

'Tut, tut, I can't have you treating good records like that.' He took it from her nerveless fingers, put it away and stood looking down at her, an unpleasant smile curving his mouth. 'Denise is coming down to Auckland with me on Sunday, as you may have guessed, and she'll be staying here tomorrow night so we can get an early start.'

'I see. She can sleep in the tapestry bedroom.' Fiona's voice was rigidly steady.

'She prefers the pink room.'

Shrugging as she moved away, she returned, 'Very well, then.' The pink room was right next to Logan's dressing room, but she was not going to worry about that! Still in measured tones she continued, 'I think I'll go up now. I feel rather tired.'

'Tired—or tired of me?'

The bored cynicism in his voice made her want to strike him, lash out at him with cruel, hurting words, but there was nothing she could say that would pierce his armour.

'A little of both, perhaps,' she retorted. 'Goodnight, Logan.'

'Oh no, you don't!'

There was such ugly meaning in his voice that her heart lurched in panic. Halfway to the door she stopped, turning to meet him as he came towards her. For a moment she was really frightened, but the expression of demonic purposefulness faded as he saw her face. 'One of these days—or nights,' he emphasised, catching her by the wrists, 'you'll push your luck too far, my darling wife. Better be careful, because when you do I'll show you no mercy.'

His lean fingers tightened cruelly, almost crushing the fragile bones of her wrists. Fiona whitened, but said coldly, 'Don't threaten me with that, Logan. You wouldn't take by force. Your ego would demand a willing surrender.'

Flames glittered deep within his eyes, making a frosty fire of them as they raked her set expression. Speaking through lips which barely moved he said harshly, 'You little fool! If I came up with you now you'd be begging me to make love to you after five minutes—just as you were before Denise rang. And don't give me any more cracks about my ego, Fiona. You flame into life when I kiss you, and however hard you might try to deny it, you know it's true. You want me as much as I want you, and don't you ever forget it!'

'Then if that's so, why don't you take me and make an end to all this—this tension?' she hissed through gritted teeth, furious with him for his ability to read her mind, even more furious with herself because her pulses were leaping at his touch.

He gave a twisted, sardonic smile. 'You'd like that, wouldn't you? Then you would have the pleasure of the physical fulfilment you want, but still consider yourself a martyr to my lust. Oh no, I'm not going to make a whip for my own back.'

He released her wrists suddenly, stepping back so that she no longer felt stifled by his nearness. Nervously she licked her lips, then with a faint shrug, changed her mind and went through the door and up the stairs to her big lonely bed. It was over two hours later that she heard him come up and go into his room. Only then did she sleep.

CHAPTER SEVEN

DENISE arrived at the indecently early hour of ten-thirty in the morning. Fiona could have snarled when she saw the car come down the drive.

As it happened she was alone in the house. Jinny had gone to see Joyce Welsh, the wife of Logan's second-in-command, and Ailsa had taken Jonathan to join the Thurstons in a picnic. When she had heard of Denise's plan to arrive that day she wondered wistfully whether she should stay behind. It had taken Fiona little effort to convince her that there was no reason for such a sacrifice of a beautiful day.

'I'm going to type up all the stuff Logan needs for the trip,' she said firmly, 'so I'll be here to greet her if she should come before you get back. And you need to get out of the house and away for the day. That headache has left you rather strained-looking. Would you like to leave Jonathan home with me?'

But Ailsa would have none of that. 'Of course not,' she retorted crisply, 'I'm quite capable of looking after him. Thank you, Fiona. I do need a day out.'

She had left in the Landrover, bearing a huge hamper with a very cheerful grandson beside her. Fiona waved him goodbye, then turned back inside the house and made a quick whip around the downstairs rooms, dusting, tidying and vacuuming, before making up the bed in the pink bedroom with pink sprigged sheets and darker pink blankets, putting out towels of the same shade and giving the room a complete scouring. It was not even dusty, for every room in the house was kept immaculate, but she was determined that Denise should find no fault whatsoever.

She heard the car come down the hill just as she was setting a bowl of camellias and jasmine on the dressing table. 'There!' she said aloud to the silent room, 'you're all ready, pink and pretty. She'll look like a rosebud here.'

Then it was off with her apron, a quick brush through her hair, and she was down, opening the door as the car came to a halt before it.

'Hullo!' Denise almost sang the word as she sprang out, vividly, vitally beautiful in a jersey dress of palest leaf green that emphasised every lovely curve and line of the slim figure beneath it. 'Why, Fiona, you look a proper little *hausfrau*! How appropriate!'

She looked around as though expecting someone else to materialise, so, not without a secret satisfaction, Fiona explained the circumstances.

'So they left you in charge,' Denise laughed as she pulled an expensive leather suitcase out of the back of her car. 'Or is Logan here to keep an eye on you?'

'No, he's over at the woolshed organising things for the shearers.'

'Yes, of course, they'll be here in a week or so. Logan told me that rain had delayed them. He was annoyed, poor darling. Where have you put me, Fiona?'

'In the pink room. Can I take your case up for you?'

'Lord no! It's not very heavy, and I don't need a wash or anything, so I'll be right down.'

She was back within five minutes, charm personified as she exclaimed over Fiona's arrangement of flowers, asked after Jonathan and laughingly hoped that Fiona wasn't cross because she had invited herself for the night.

Cross! Fiona thought even as she smiled a disclaimer, unconsciously echoing Logan the night before. 'No, why should I be? Much the most sensible arrangement. Are you planning a shopping trip?'

'We-ell, yes and no. I've decided to buy myself a new dress for your party, and I have to see the dentist. When Logan told me he was going down it seemed the ideal arrangement for us to travel together, petrol being the price it is. You're not coming?'

As if she didn't know! 'No, it's my day as a mother's help

at Play Centre on Monday, and I can't put them off.'

Fiona led the way through the drawing room out on to the terrace where the tea-tray stood on one of the wrought iron tables. She had made tea and coffee while Denise was upstairs, and now asked her which she would prefer.

'Oh, coffee, thanks.' Subsiding gracefully on to one of the loungers, Denise looked up at her hostess, slimly elegant in a perfectly plain shirtwaister of dark blue cotton, the tailored lines of the dress enhancing her still beauty. Abruptly Denise asked, 'Does your skin ever tan, Fiona? Or do you remain lily-pale all through the summer?'

'Oh, I tan.' Fiona brought the coffee across, settled it on the small table beside the lounger and went on, 'Not very much, and I have to be careful, but I'm not always lily-pale!'

'It's just as well Jonathan has the olive Sutherland skin,' Denise remarked idly, looking round her with what could only be read as complacency. 'He'll be able to take our Northern sun without burning. Logan can—he goes a glorious shade of dark brown in the summer.'

'Lucky Logan,' Fiona returned lightly, seating herself not too far away to be polite, yet not close enough for confidences. Denise looked like a lovely cat in the lounger, basking with sybaritic delight in the warmth of the sun. Just like an advertisement for terrace furniture, Fiona thought irrepressibly, and so much at home!

That hint of complacency with which the girl looked around her had not been lost on her unwilling hostess. It was as though Denise was seeing herself as mistress here. Moved by an ignoble impulse, she went on to say, 'It's to be hoped that any other children we have are born with the same suitable Sutherland skin, then.'

There was a sudden stillness about the figure opposite her, before Denise said with elaborate casualness, 'Yes. Are you planning to have others?'

Fiona allowed a small smile, which she hoped looked reminiscent, to play around her lips. 'Well—Logan is—he would like to have more. He thinks that Jonathan has been cock of the roost for long enough. And certainly Ailsa would love more grandchildren to dote on.' She looked up at the pergola, ostensibly gazing at the tender new leaves on the ancient grapevine which would make the terrace cool and shaded over the summer, but the smile on her lips was very definitely that of a woman who is thinking of sensual delights she has no intention of discussing.

There was an odd little silence, then a cup rattled as if a careless hand had knocked it—or trembled holding it. Denise said idly, 'So Logan is thinking of founding a dynasty! How do you feel about it?'

'Oh, quite happy. One gets cumbersome, of course, but the end results are very worthwhile.'

A tinkling little laugh, then in acid sweet tones Denise asked, 'It doesn't worry you, then, that Logan thinks of you in the same way as he thinks of his breeding cows? I should hate it, myself. When I marry I want to be the most important person in my husband's life, more important to him than any children I shall give him.'

And that's a coup to you, Fiona thought wryly, acknowledging the hit which had landed with exquisite precision right where her nerves were most sensitive. Not a sign of this showed in the smooth, almost creamy face as she replied, 'I don't think Logan regards me in exactly the same light as his breeding stock. There are—certain differences.'

Denise set her cup firmly on the table, stretched languorously and placed her hands behind her head, smiling oddly. 'It's always intrigued me, this business of people being attracted to each other. There must have been a positive explosion between you two for you to have defied your parents and married him so quickly. After all, he was only away that year for six weeks! And yet there's no sign of it now! You must be able to cover your feelings very well; no one knows what Logan is feeling, of course, but I expected the air to positively sizzle between you.'

She laughed charmingly, but the dark eyes were shrewd and watchful as they rested on Fiona's pure profile. 'They say that still waters run deep. I hope that's so for Logan's sake, for he has that extraordinary virility that is so magnetic.' She paused, then drove her point home. 'Does it worry you to know that he was unfaithful to you? I'm not supposed to know, of course, but this is such a small place, and one can't help but hear the gossip. And somehow, it makes a man seem even more exciting when one knows he's experienced when it comes to love. It must make him a much better husband.'

You started it, Fiona told herself, and you deserve everything you get. You should have known better than to think you could take her on and win. Aloud, she replied with serene composure, 'When I left him I gave up any rights I ever had to figure in his life at all, so no, nothing he did in the years we were apart worries me.'

'Perhaps you had one or two adventures yourself.' Denise's voice was slyly insinuating, yet completely friendly. 'I'm sure no one would blame you, although men have funny ideas, don't they? I mean, I can imagine Logan thinking it was perfectly all right for him to make love to any willing female—and who wouldn't be willing with Logan?—but he might be very angry if you took the same licence.'

Almost, Fiona relaxed. Denise might be hoping to lull her into making foolish confidences, but she would find nothing like that in Fiona's past. Indeed, she had never felt the least interest in any other man.

'Well, it doesn't arise,' she replied calmly.

'What, not one tiny indiscretion?' A tiny chuckle. 'Faithful Griselda indeed! How noble of you, especially when there was really no reason for you to remain quite so wedded to his memory.'

Did she know about that belated wedding ceremony? It would be the sheerest bad luck if someone had seen them, but certainly Denise was hinting at something. There was no mistaking the meaningful glance. Fiona retaliated with a mildly astonished lift of her eyebrows.

It seemed, however, that Denise was not yet ready to reveal her knowledge, for she looked slight confusion and hurried on with a sly smile, 'I mean, as far as you knew you would never see him again. It was a terrific coincidence your meeting him in Wellington, wasn't it? Coincidences have a way of happening at the oddest times. I'll bet you felt like Cinderella when he whisked you up here—I believe you were living in a dreadful place, almost a slum.' Her voice invested the word with visions of dirt and sordid drudgery.

'Not quite,' Fiona managed to say, wondering if Logan had told her that, then dismissing the thought with the contempt it deserved. He was not a man to discuss his wife behind her back, especially not with his ex-girl-friend. Denise was merely trying to sow dissension between them.

'Well, certainly nothing like this,' the other girl observed. 'It must have been wonderful for you when you realised just how rich Logan is. He said you had a terrific spending spree in Wellington. Lucky you!'

Anger grew deep within Fiona, but she repressed it sternly. 'Yes, I've been very lucky. But I think it's Jonathan who has benefited most by the change in our circumstances.'

There was no mistaking the alteration in Denise's expression at this remark. Fiona stared, and thought in amazement, why, the girl is really fond of him!

'Yes. That ghastly cough has gone,' Denise said happily, 'and I'm positive he's grown taller. He's going to be just as tall as Logan, I'm sure, and every bit as husky. I suppose, as his mother, you feel that any sacrifice is worthwhile for him.'

There was an odd note in the clear high tones, a curious questioning.

'Yes,' Fiona said steadily, her eyes meeting her opponent's with transparent honesty in their grey depths. 'Any sacrifice at all.'

Denise jumped up from the lounger, laughing delightedly. 'That's exactly what I expected you to say. I'm sure, Fiona, no one could query your love for him! It must be a very powerful emotion, mother love.'

'It's not even an emotion. It's part of you, at the core of your being, and it permeates your whole life.' Fiona stopped, a rueful smile touching her lips. 'Dear me, how pompous that sounds! It's true, nevertheless.'

'Of course,' Denise agreed absently, moving across to the balustrade. She looked down the garden with possessive pleasure, smiling that secret, almost smug smile which came to her at odd times when she was at Whangatapu. It had never been in evidence when her eyes rested on Logan, but occasionally there had been a leaping response in the girl's expression when he spoke to her which made Fiona embarrassed and jealous and oddly sad for her. For Logan had said that the Sutherlands did not divorce, so Denise's hopeful but discreet pursuit was doomed to failure.

'Oh, there's Logan now,' Denise exclaimed, laughing and waving her hand as he came round the corner of the house. 'Hi, Logan! Come and have a cup of tea!' She was alight suddenly, the blood running free through her veins, and for one long moment all her dreams and hopes were vivid in her face as she watched him walk with his lithe silent footsteps towards the terrace.

Fiona averted her head from this shameless radiance, poured out tea as Logan liked it, without milk or sugar. She did not see them meet, for Denise ran down the steps to him, but when they came up on to the terrace the other girl was clinging to his arm and laughing.

Fiona could not stop the somewhat contemptuous look that cooled her smile. He had no right to do this to Denise, no right at all. Surely he could make her see that her pursuit of him was hopeless, that she was wasting her youth in a vain dream. He saw the condemnation in her eyes. Without stopping in his stride he put Denise aside and bent to Fiona, touching her mouth with careless mastery in a kiss that was quite definitely a punishment.

When he lifted his head he was smiling, more than a hint of arrogance in his voice as he said, 'Hullo, darling; playing ladies, when there's a stack of typing in my study a mile high?'

Anger sparkled in the transparent depths of her eyes, but she managed to stay creditably composed under the knowledgeable smile. It did not help that Denise's mouth was compressed beneath eyes that glittered with fury.

'It will get done,' she murmured. 'Here's your tea.'

'Good, I'm as dry as a wooden god. How's your mother, Denise?' turning to her with that effortless charm which immediately cooled her temper.

'Oh, the doctor wants her to see a specialist in town. He doesn't think anything is seriously wrong with her, but he wants to be sure. Poor Mummy, she's in a terrible dither. Daddy wants her to go away on a cruise with him, but she doesn't seem to be able to make up her mind about what she wants to do. There's me, you see. I don't want to go with them if they're going on a second honeymoon, but they'll worry if I stay alone here.'

'Stay here,' Logan suggested lightly. 'Fiona would be glad to have you, and you know I don't have to speak for my mother. She has always loved having you.'

Punishment, Fiona thought savagely, forcing herself to smile and second the invitation with all the cordiality she could muster.

'But how marvellous!' Denise was ecstatic, more than slightly high on pleasure. Impulsively she swung herself up to kiss Logan's cheek, before laughing delightedly across at Fiona. 'Forgive me, my dear, for stealing that, but it's a perfect scheme! Mummy will have no qualms about leaving me here in Logan's care, and I just love staying at Whangatapu. Thank you, Logan, for thinking of it.'

As if you hadn't engineered it, Fiona thought ironically, torn by a jealousy as primitive as it was futile. I just hope you know what you're doing, my darling husband.

Ailsa was delighted with the idea; and she went immediately to the telephone to suggest it to Mrs Page. And Mrs Page was delighted too, apparently. So was Jonathan, when Denise asked him if he would like to have her stay for a few days. In fact, everyone wallowed in delight. Fiona went off to the kitchen to attack the dinner preparation.

'You're supposed to be peeling those potatoes, not killing them,' Jinny remarked drily.

'Substituting them for something else,' Fiona retorted.

'Fair enough; kneading bread dough is better, but I suppose those poor spuds can take it. You'll have to get over it, you know. The Sutherlands have always been hospitable.'

Fiona snorted, running cold water over the de-jacketed potatoes. 'Even if it kills them, I suppose.'

Jinny sniffed, but said, 'Well, just remember that you're the hostess here. She can't take over if you don't let her.'

The potatoes were deposited into a saucepan, salted, watered and placed on the huge electric stove. 'That's all very well, but——' Fiona sighed, then went on, 'Well, if I can let off steam here it won't be so bad, I guess. Why are you so good to me, Jinny?'

'For the family's sake,' Jinny said shortly. 'At first, anyway. It irritates me to see anyone as gormless as you seem to be trying to cope. I've always had a weakness for fools, I suppose.'

Fiona laughed, and dropped a kiss on the housekeeper's cheek, the first time she had ever dared such intimacy. 'I do love you,' she said, 'you're just what I need to keep my feet very firmly on the ground.'

'Get away with you!' An unbecoming flush had mantled Jinny's cheek, but her rejoinder was given in a gentler voice that Fiona had ever heard her use. 'You're a soft thing, but you know how to get round a body. Why don't you try it on Logan?'

Jinny, of course, would know that they did not share a bed, for she knew everything that went on in the homestead, but it was the first time she had ever referred to the situation, even indirectly.

Fiona flushed, but could not find words to answer.

'None of my business.' Jinny took pity on her obvious embarrassment. 'But he's only a man, and it's easy for a man to love where his wants lie.'

'I don't—I want more than that,' Fiona said in a low voice.

'Well, you know best, I suppose.' Jinny smiled dourly. 'Now go and get changed for dinner. And remember who you are, for heaven's sake.'

So Fiona changed into a chiffon in a misty floral print of blues and greens, dabbed on an exotic perfume Logan had bought her in Rotorua, and chased Jonathan around her bedroom, threatening him with the stopper. His squeals and laughter brought Logan in, half changed but bare-torsoed; he laughed and snatched Fiona's hand away, twisting it behind her back.

'Girls' stuff!' Jonathan teased, dancing around in front of them. 'I'm not a girl!'

'No, you certainly are not.' Logan's eyes dwelt on him for a moment, then turned to Fiona's laughing face. She was doing her best to look indignant at his high-handed method of stopping their game, but her pulses were racing. Their glances met and locked; she tipped the bottle on to the finger of her free hand, brought it up and dabbed the sweet musky perfume on to the brown hollow in Logan's throat.

Jonathan squealed with horror and laughter. 'You smell like a lady, Daddy! Naughty Mummy!'

'Naughty Mummy indeed,' Logan said lazily. 'How shall I punish her, Jonathan?'

Their son chuckled wickedly. Like all children he loved to savour the idea of punishing his mother. 'Smack her hand?' he suggested.

'No, I have a better idea. You take the perfume from her hand, Jonno, so that she won't spill it.'

Little fingers grasped the flask. Jonathan bore it triumphantly away, while Fiona tried vainly to look cool and insouciant. It was impossible, for Logan's mouth was curved in a cynical smile as his eyes roved her flushed face, and she could not meet the insolent appraisal.

'What are you going to do, Daddy?'

'I'm going to kiss her,' Logan said, bringing her hard up against him.

Jonathan said disappointedly, 'But she likes it when you kiss her.'

'I'm going to kiss her very hard,' Logan told him solemnly. 'Like this.'

His mouth swooped, crushing hers with purposeful demand. The blood drummed in her ears. Her arms came up to his shoulders, smoothing the sleek skin across his back, then Jonathan burrowed in between them, wriggling his way in until Logan broke away and picked him up. Two strong little arms twined round their necks, bringing their mouths together again.

'Now you can kiss each other properly,' Jonathan said in satisfied tones.

Tears sprang into Fiona's eyes. She leaned her head against Logan's chest, all passion gone, aware only that it was broad enough for both her and Jonathan to rest on.

'Soggy with sentimentality,' his amused voice said in her ear.

She laughed, choked and said back, 'You do smell sweet, my darling.'

There was an odd little silence, then, 'That's the first endearment you've ever called me,' he said. 'I think it deserves a reward.'

Setting Jonathan down, he told him to go and get the little parcel on the chest of drawers in the next room. While they waited he kept his arm round her shoulders, holding her firmly but without force. She relaxed against him, resisting a strong impulse to run her fingers through the fine curly hair that grew on his chest, contenting herself with the feel of his arm across her bared shoulders.

'Have I seen that dress before?' he asked. 'It's pretty, and it suits you.'

'You made me buy it, in Wellington.'

He nodded, 'I remember. I was right to insist. It makes you look like a water witch.'

'You are poetic!' she teased.

His arm tightened, but Jonathan's reappearance prevented any move on his part. Fiona watched with doting eyes as he carried the small white box carefully across the room and gave it to his father. She could not repress a gasp when Logan snapped the ring box open, for inside rested a huge rose diamond, so exquisitely set in platinum that it did not look over-large or ostentatious.

'It came back today,' Logan said, slipping it on to her finger. He slanted her a mocking look, before lifting her hand to kiss first the ring and then her palm.

Greatly shaken, she murmured, 'Oh . . . it's beautiful! Is it really pink?'

'Yes. Your hand graces it, Fiona.'

Flushing, she looked up at him. The mockery had fled from his expression, leaving a new gravity which bewildered her.

'I . . . thank you, Logan,' she said quietly. On impulse she stretched up and kissed his cheek.

He was very still, then he returned, 'I can see that I'd better make a habit of giving you jewellery, if that's going to be your reaction. Who knows what you might be persuaded to give for a diamond necklace!'

'It's not the ring,' she said quickly, before he laughed at her horrified expression and dropped a careless arm about her shoulders once more.

'I know that! Now, release me so that I can get into the rest of my clothes, or I'll be late for dinner. Come on, Jonathan, and I'll put some after-shave on your face. Much better than Mummy's perfume.'

'Just like yours?'

'Just like mine,' Logan promised gravely.

For a few moments Fiona stood staring after them, before she stirred herself to comb a stray lock of hair into place. Logan had disarranged it, and as Denise was almost certain to be exquisitely neat she could not go down with her hair in a mess.

Denise, of course, noticed the ring as soon as she came into the room. Fiona, seeing those dark eyes fixed unblinkingly on the glittering ring, had to resist a ridiculous impulse to shield it with her other hand. Then Denise looked up, and there was no expression at all in her face, not a flicker of animation. She looked for all the world like a doll, beautifully made up and dressed, but lacking any spark of life. It came back, however, when Logan came in with Jonathan.

Reluctantly, Fiona admitted to herself that when she chose to, Denise took the limelight without appearing to try to. She effervesced, turning the time before dinner into a sort of mini-party, laughing, witty, using all of the allure of her beauty and charm to capture everyone's attention and win their response. And respond they did, from Jonathan to Forrest Thurston; Denise even charmed his wife from her normal placid down-to-earth manner to reveal that she was an accomplished raconteur with a fund of stories culled from all over the globe.

Relegated once more to the outside, Fiona thought bitterly; then, damn her, she won't get away with it. The thought of that oddly intimate scene upstairs came back to her. Without realising it she smiled. Logan intercepted it from next to Denise, smiled back, and left the circle to come across to Fiona, whose heart threatened to swell and burst at the splendid physical presence of him.

'Hi,' he said softly, 'what's so interesting?' for Fiona had appeared to be staring at some knick-knacks in a glass-topped table.

'This medal,' she returned, improvising quickly. 'What is it? I can see "Logan Sutherland", but I'm sure you didn't go to World War One.'

He grinned. 'My grandfather. Do you like the snuffbox next to it? That enamelled one with the Cupid swooping down on a pair of lovers?'

'It's very pretty.'

A crack of laughter came from across the room, then Denise's light voice calling, 'Are you two talking secrets?'

'Just having a marital discussion,' Logan said urbanely.

The dark eyes ranged speculatively over them. 'Is Fiona

worrying you about the dinner arrangements? Poor Logan, how are the mighty fallen! I thought all that you ever did was snap your fingers and things were done.'

Quite deliberately Logan dropped his arm over his wife's shoulders, pulling her close beside him. Before he could say anything Ailsa hurried into the conversation.

'What time are you planning to leave tomorrow, you two?' she asked.

'At the crack of dawn.' Denise's voice held a note which could almost have been termed shrill.

'Six o'clock,' came Logan's deep tones, imperturbable as ever.

Fiona found herself chuckling. 'So it will be a five o'clock rising for us. I'll send Jonathan in to you, Denise. He always wakes me up with a kiss, much nicer than an alarm clock.'

'I'll give you a butterfly kiss,' Jonathan told Denise, beaming up at her.

Tension dissipated immediately. Denise bent, touching his head with real affection. 'I'd love that, darling. But are you awake at five o'clock every morning?'

'Most mornings,' Logan said drily. 'Fortunately he's been trained not to wake anyone else. Probably because his mother is so bad-tempered that she doesn't speak until she's had two cups of coffee.'

'Oh—liar!' Fiona exaggerated her indignation, raising a reproachful face to meet the wicked amusement in his. 'Bad-tempered indeed! I just don't wake up quickly!'

'Bad-tempered,' Logan reiterated.

Mrs Thurston drained her sherry glass and said briskly, 'I know what you mean, Logan, because I'm like that too. But have you ever thought how painful it is for people like us to be confronted with a disgustingly hearty type every morning?'

The conversation became general. Logan moved to refill glasses, Forrest embroiled Denise in a discussion on an art exhibition currently showing at one of the galleries in Auckland, and Ailsa and Mrs Thurston and Fiona chatted comfortably about Ailsa's latest book, which was not going well, or so the anxious author thought.

Dinner passed off reasonably well, but there was another awkward moment when Logan picked up Jonathan, who had been allowed to stay up for a treat, to carry him off to bed.

The small black head nodded against Logan's chest, then Jonathan straightened up and said with a sleepy chuckle, 'Daddy, you do smell nice! You didn't wash off Mummy's perfume.'

'Neither I did.'

It would have ended there, except that Denise asked incredulously, 'Don't tell me you swipe Fiona's perfume for after-shave, Logan!'

'Mummy sloshed it on him,' Jonathan informed her. 'But she didn't get any on me. And Daddy said he was going to punish her, but he only kissed her, and she likes that.' His clear tones still held a tinge of disappointment. 'Still,' he added with satisfaction, 'Daddy said it was a very hard kiss.'

Everybody laughed, Denise's ringing out over the rest.

'What antics you get up to!' she murmured. Her fingers were white around the stem of the brandy glass, the glance she cast at Fiona glittering with dislike. 'Somehow I can't imagine you joining in nursery games, Logan. It seems—not in your image.'

Logan looked faintly amused, never so masculine as now, with his son resting confidently in his arms. 'Have I an image? You've been reading too much newspaper guff on politicians, Denise. Come on, Fiona, let's get this child to bed before he drops off. He's as heavy as lead.'

After that there was an indefinable tension in the air. To her credit, Denise hid her chagrin very well, but took herself off to bed early because of the early start the next morning. Perhaps, too, because Logan and Fiona had gone into the study.

Logan surprised his wife by saying, once they had got there, 'I've made sure that Joe is well clued up on what's going on, Fiona, but he'll come to you if anything goes wrong. You can rely on him completely, so follow his advice.'

Fiona nodded. Joe Welsh was the oldest of the farm workers, a serious hard-working man who was Logan's second-in-command at Whangatapu. He spoke little, but what he did say was short and to the point, and she knew that Logan trusted him.

'Nothing can go wrong, can it?' she asked a little timidly.

He smiled. 'On a farm, anything can go wrong! But don't worry. Here's the phone number of the hotel where I'm staying, the Central; you'll reach me there in the mornings, and I'll ring each evening just to check up. You'll cope, so don't worry. Just one thing—keep away from Danny. Joe tells me he's boiling up for something.'

She looked up sharply. 'Which means ...?'

'God knows.' Frowning, Logan passed a hand across the back of his neck, pushing his head against it so that the tough line of his jaw became vividly emphasised. 'He fancies himself to be in love with Denise, but she's not interested. He won't like the fact that she's going to Auckland with me.'

Sheer shock robbed her of speech for a moment. So that was why Danny was so bitter! Logan's original sin, or what he conceived to be sin, had been compounded by a hopeless passion for Denise. 'Poor Danny,' she said distressfully.

'Pity him if you like, but keep away from him. Have I your promise?'

Surprised at the harshness of his voice, she nodded. 'Yes, of course. I don't like him overmuch, though I can't help feeling sorry for him.'

'You would feel sorry for the devil himself,' he said grimly. 'Your compassion doesn't extend to me, however.'

A rare note of tiredness stirred her heart. She came up to him, resting the hand where the rose diamond glittered above her wedding ring on the dark stuff of his sleeve. 'Poor Logan,' she said, mischief colouring her voice. 'Is it compassion you want from me?'

His frown cleared. 'No, by God, it is not, and well you know it.' His hand covered hers. 'Why don't you let yourself fall in love with me, Fiona? Is it pride, or independence, or just sheer bloody-mindedness?'

'A mixture of all three, I suppose.' She spoke lightly, but the underlying seriousness of her words came through strongly. 'Oh, I know it would make things easier for all of us, but you want things made too easy for you.'

'Yes, I suppose I do. And yet'—with a glinting smile that nearly overset her defences—'I enjoy the hunt, too. It adds a certain savour to life, waiting for your capitulation.'

'You said, not so long ago, that you wouldn't wait for that, that you would let me salvage my pride by making the decision yours.'

'I've changed my mind, darling. The decision will have to be entirely yours. You're not the woman to be won by rough wooing, and quite frankly, I wouldn't find much satisfaction in it. I know that you want me—I've known it from the first, just as I've known that I could take you any time I wanted to. Besides, if you remember all that I've said so clearly, you must recollect that I also said that I wouldn't make love to you against your will because it would allow you to consider yourself a martyr to my unbridled masculine lust. Any easy out for you, Fiona, is not what you're going to get.'

She sighed, a wave of depression almost making her admit her love and take the consequences. Why did she have to be so foolish as to demand the moon and the stars, when Logan offered a very reasonable substitute? Only—it was just a substitute, and if she surrendered she would always be racked by jealousy and the knowledge that some vital part of her happiness was missing.

'Yes, I'm a hard man,' he said, disconcerting her by the occasional way he had of reaching her mind. 'But you knew that, Fiona, when you came up here as my wife. And it's a compliment really. You can't deny that I respect your rights as a person.'

Respect is no substitute for love, she said, but she did not say it aloud, and then her love made her become stern and wifely.

'You're tired,' she said, 'and you have an early start in the morning.'

'In the words of Pepys, "and so to bed!"' He smiled rather narrowly, but dropped a light kiss on her forehead. 'Goodnight, Fiona.'

CHAPTER EIGHT

THE beach at Whangatapu was long and golden, curved like a slice of rock melon on a blue and green platter. At the opposite end to that where the jetty and the boat ramp were situated, the creek debouched shallowly across the sand from a small lagoon set about with great flax bushes. It was a splendid place to play Spacemen, and that was what Jonathan was doing now with the two Welsh boys, all of them armed with the long dry sticks of the flax flowers which made excellent ray guns.

Fiona lay relaxed in the shade of a huge, gnarled pohutukawa tree, for the spring sun was hot when there was no wind to temper it. A book lay open beside her, but she was too sleepy to read. The high excited voices of the children rang on the still air as they ambushed Martians all through the flax bushes, occasionally dropping to an excited murmur when they met to confer together.

Out in the harbour a small yacht tacked to and fro somewhat erratically. It looked distinctly overloaded; not surprising, since Janey Welsh, aged ten, was learning to sail under the watchful tutelage of her older brother, and the little P-class yacht was very definitely a one-man boat. It was an ideal day for a novice skipper, very little wind and that gentle, so that she had no chance of being frightened before she learned enough about it to be confident.

The sturdy massif of the Mount of the Warriors blued with the first of the summer's heat haze, the tiny trig height on the summit glittering white in the sun's rays. Seagulls screeched, a gannet dived, gold head first, into the water in search of fish, and popped up a moment or so later apparently satisfied, because it stretched its wings and flew slowly away across the harbour to the northern shore where, presumably, its mate was waiting.

Fiona yawned, but resisted the temptation to close her eyes. Logan was coming home this afternoon, and she was not going to be asleep when he arrived. He had been away for four days, he and Denise, and Fiona had become one ache of emptiness without him. Telephone calls, though reassuring, were definitely no substitute for the real thing, she thought.

Everything had gone like clockwork. Joe came up to the house once a day to tell her solemnly that everything was fine, Ailsa had rescued her manuscript from its difficulties, and the Thurstons still sketched and drew all round the station. And although she had seen Danny, he had made no attempts to speak to her other than exchanging greetings. Jinny and Fiona were well away with preparations for the party on Saturday, and in the garden the silken blooms of early summer were already hiding the gaps left by the spring bulbs. Even her mother's help day at the Play Centre had been a joy. The children were charming, the two other mothers she met there were very pleasant indeed after the initial stiffness had worn off.

Fiona felt that she was, perhaps, beginning to find her feet in the district. Her position at Whangatapu seemed secure now. At first she had hoped only for tolerance, for Jonathan's sake, but unless she was entirely misreading things, she had gained liking from both Ailsa and Jinny. Lukewarm, it might be, but at least it was more than she had expected to achieve on that first day, which now seemed so long ago. Indeed, the past seemed to have receded to a distant blur in her memory. That time when she had struggled to give Jonathan some semblance of a normal life was already almost forgotten.

An ironic smile touched her lips. How security wrapped one in a warm blanket, an insulation from the pain and worry that had seemed an integral part of her being only a few short months ago! Pain there still was, of a kind, and worry too, but there was no doubt that she was much more content than she had been for years. Not exactly happy, for her love for Logan gnawed at her emotions, and she was bitterly jealous of Denise. Whatever relationship they had had in the past was certainly over, but one of Fiona's bitterest mental queries was whether Logan remembered it with regret. Useless to attempt to convince herself that he had not kissed those inviting lips, shared moments of passion with her, even if the desire had not been fulfilled. All that she knew was that Logan would hear nothing against Denise, and his wife's angry words about the girl had provoked his brutal retaliation. She would not be so stupid again! It would be constant gall to know that to Logan Denise Page was somehow sacrosanct, but she must learn to endure it.

Listlessly she picked up a handful of sand. Three days of hot sun had removed the dampness from the top layer, so that it ran freely through her fingers. The children shrieked with laughter, then fell silent. Someone was walking across the grass towards her, she could hear the soft thud of feet and looked up hopefully, but it was not Logan who appeared on the bank which separated land from beach.

Danny put a hand on the overhanging branch of the pohutukawa tree and vaulted down to the sand, rocked a moment as his feet sank into the soft depths, then straightened up to come purposefully towards her. Beneath the somewhat tattered cotton hat he wore his expression was grave, as though he was not at all sure of his welcome.

'Hullo,' he said, stopping a few feet away from her.

Fiona sat up, glad that she had not been lured by the sun into wearing anything too revealing. As it was, her shorts suddenly seemed too scanty, her legs too long and bare.

'Hullo, is anything the matter?' she asked with reserve.

'No, nothing's wrong. I came to apologise about the way I baled you up that day. I've been looking for a chance for some time.'

Drawing her legs up so that she could rest her chin on them, Fiona thought fleetingly of Logan's injunction not to have anything to do with Danny. Common courtesy and the profound sympathy she felt for him dictated her reply.

'Don't worry about it, Danny.'

'I am worrying,' he said frankly. 'It was inexusable of me to behave like a boor, and I must admit I did it for the worst reasons. I didn't really think of your reactions, or how it must have hurt you. Please forgive me.'

He was so sincere, looked so concerned, that Fiona thawed. 'Of course I do. Don't think anything more of it.' She looked up, a half smile on her lips, met the full force of his gaze and blinked. No one could mistake the admiration there—Fiona had seen it often before in men's eyes—but there was also a kind of bleak loneliness that wrung her heart. Poor Danny, so bound up in the chains of hatred he had forged for himself that he was living in a kind of hell. Unrequited love, as she well knew, was the most lonely of emotions.

'Thank you,' he said quietly. 'I feel a lot better now, though I know I don't deserve it.' He hesitated, obviously wondering whether to go, then sat down on the sand, still several feet away from her. 'Are you looking forward to this party? It will be the first time you meet most of the Sutherlands' friends, won't it?'

'Yes, it will be, and I am looking forward to it.' Not even to herself would she admit that part of her wanted to shrivel up and die at the thought of all those curious people.

He nodded. 'I'd have thought, myself, that it would be easier to meet them in ones and twos, but I guess you'll get the whole ordeal over in one fell swoop, so to speak. I'll be there, too.' He gave her a direct look and a singularly sweet smile. 'I won't create a fuss, I promise you, so don't worry. I have very good company manners.'

Here was another man who seemed able to read her thoughts! Fiona shrugged. 'I hadn't thought you would.'

'No, I don't believe you had,' he said slowly. 'You haven't that sort of mind, I'm sure.'

Into the silence caused by Fiona's inability to think of any answer to that came the noise of the children's play. Danny grinned, jerking his head towards the lagoon. 'Enjoying themselves, aren't they? Young Jonathan's a real boy. Neat seat on a horse, too, for a youngster.'

'Don't tell me,' Fiona said quickly. 'It's going to be a surprise. I'm not allowed to know how he's getting on. I think he hopes he'll be able to astound me with his skill!'

'Oh, he'll do that, I'm sure.'

Another silence, but this time it had more of companionship in it. Danny hauled a packet of cigarettes out of his pocket, offered them to her, and at her refusal lit one for himself.

'Makes you think summer's just about here, doesn't it,' he mused from behind the cloud of smoke. 'Ever been through a Northland summer?'

'No. No, I haven't.'

'You'll notice the heat, I suppose. I did, when I came up here, and so did Mary. You get acclimatised, of course, but the first summer is usually a bit wearing. There's lots doing, too. Guests at the homestead, and the baches are always full.'

'Baches?' It was a word new to Fiona.

'Cribs, they call them in the South Island. Holiday homes, beach houses. The four along Ocean Beach are loaned to friends from Auckland or further south. That was how we got to know the Sutherlands, through mutual friends in Auckland who arranged for us to stay in one of them. We had a fabulous three weeks. That was three years ago.'

He inhaled deeply, then went on, 'Then the whole thing blew up in our faces. Still, that's not any worry of yours. I actually had another thing to ask of you. When Mary comes, will you try to be friends with her? She needs someone in the family to like her. I think you and she might have things in common, and she's not happy. I may be a lout, Mrs Sutherland, but I love my sister, and I'd give my life to make her happy.'

'I doubt if she'd ask such a sacrifice of you,' Fiona said, strongly moved by the appeal in his voice. She rose, picking up the rug before she said quietly, 'If your sister is willing, I'll be glad to be friends with her.'

'She'll be willing,' he stated with bleak certainty. He had risen as soon as she did, and stood looking down at her, to all outward appearances a handsome, serious man with a problem she could solve for him. 'She has no friends in the family; you'd know how lonely that is.'

Fiona opened her mouth to speak, then closed it firmly. That last remark sounded very close to a probe, and her situation at the homestead was no business of his. So she smiled and said lightly, 'Oh, I've settled in properly now. I'll have to go, if you will excuse me.'

'Sure. I'd better be off too, or I might get the sack. I'll take the rug for you.'

She could not refuse him, so they walked side by side back to the homestead, Fiona calling to Jonathan as they went.

Logan and Denise arrived back half an hour later, as Fiona was sliding a leg of lamb into the oven. The first intimation she had was Jonathan's joyous shriek from outside when he recognised the car.

'Off with you,' said Jinny, not pausing from rolling out yards of flaky pastry.

Fiona took off her apron and fled; at the front door she stopped, took a deep breath, then opened it and walked sedately down the steps just as the big car drew up on the gravel.

Jonathan was there before her, of course, laughing with excitement as he tugged at the door handle. Grinning, Logan opened the door, got out and swept him up in a bear-hug from which he emerged tousled and breathless. Then Logan saw Fiona and came up the steps two at a time to catch her close and kiss her soundly. Her hand caught the lapels of his coat as she responded with all of her heart. He lifted his head, smiled, and said softly, 'Everything O.K.?'

Bemused, she nodded as her hands dropped to her side. 'Everything is fine. And you?'

'I did all I wanted to, and I'm glad to be back home.'

Denise's laughing voice broke in on them, causing them to pull apart almost guiltily. 'Marriage has done nothing for your manners, Logan,' she purred from behind him. 'I had to let myself out of the car.'

As he moved aside with a quick apology Fiona caught sight of the other girl, and almost reeled with shock, for Denise was languorous, sleek as a well-fed cat, her smile brilliant, her eyes lazy and satisfied as they rested with unmistakable meaning on Logan. And he—Fiona saw the quick frown he gave Denise, as though to warn her, and felt the shattering pain of betrayal strike like a dagger to her heart. She wanted to scream, to slap Denise across her beautiful face, to curse and shout and rave, but of course she was Logan Sutherland's wife, and she could not do any of those things. So she unclenched her hands and said with no expression in her voice, 'You must be thirsty. Would you like something to drink?'

'Love it,' Denise murmured serenely. Apparently that quick contraction of Logan's brows had had its effect, for she was no longer the woman in possession, preening herself in front of her lover, but the good friend of the family as she greeted Ailsa and drank tea and told them that her parents were in Auckland to see her mother's specialist, so she would have to trespass on their hospitality for one more night.

In direct contrast to the evening before they had left for Auckland Denise was almost subdued, but that possessive gleam was never absent from her eyes, even though she didn't once look directly at Logan, or he at her, and there were long moments when she sat silent, a sensuous half-smile curving her lips. Perhaps she was remembering—Fiona pushed the thought from her mind and concentrated on her duties as a hostess. At last it was time to retire and her taut nerves were stretched almost to snapping point.

Logan did not go up with the rest of them; he said he had a few loose ends to tidy up and went off to the study, leaving Fiona torn with an agony of indecision. Should she go down and have it out with him? Common sense came to her aid. What was there to have out? A look exchanged, a moment of time when Denise had exuded sexual satisfaction—Logan would sneer her out of court! Desperately she tried to convince herself that she had been mistaken, that this was one more subtle trick of Denise's, but that awareness which every woman has about the man she loves made such a conviction impossible.

Still fully clothed, she sat on the bed in the darkness of her room, hands pressed to her temples to try and block out the hideous pictures that seemed to have taken over her brain. At last, exhausted and with a raging headache, she forced herself to face facts, ugly though they might be. And, oddly, the mere facing of them seemed to rob them of some of their power to hurt.

So Logan and Denise had become lovers. Well, Denise was certainly not the first woman in his life. Possibly she would not be the last. Unlikely as it seemed it was possible that he found women irresistible, and if the girl threw herself at him, as she was quite capable of doing, then perhaps that control she had thought unbreakable had snapped.

She faced another fact head-on. Possibly she had been wrong all along, and he did love Denise. In which case she had done them both a great wrong in marrying Logan, but not as great a wrong as he had accomplished by turning his back on the woman he loved out of a mistaken sense of duty to his son. It was his determination that Jonathan should grow up a Sutherland which had brought about this whole mess, and because of Jonathan he would never let her go.

Unless she left Jonathan behind.

The idea leapt full-blown into Fiona's tortured mind. Biting her lips until the blood ran, she tried and failed to push it away, but it took stronger and stronger hold, until she gave a whimpering sigh, defeated by it. That would be the only way to free Logan and make him happy—but, oh God, at what a cost to her!

Nausea gripped her, then the blood rushed to her head. She could not think straight, could no longer hold back the black shadow of despair, but sleep, which had never seemed so sweet, would be unattainable in her present state. Walking like an old woman, she groped her way across the room. In a locked cabinet in the main bathroom were Ailsa's sleeping pills. If she took one of those it would give her the oblivion she craved.

The dim wall bracket in the hall gave just enough light to see by. Cautiously, in case Logan should hear her, she crept along the thick carpet, took the sleeping pills, then made her way back. At the head of the stairs she looked down and saw her husband and Denise locked in a fierce embrace under the one light that gleamed in the hall below.

Without stopping she walked on into her bedroom, changed into her nightgown and crawled into bed, to lie shaken and sick to her heart's core.

When the tap came on the door she lay still, hoping that Logan would believe she was asleep. But he opened it, and switched the light on, saying quietly, 'I know that you're awake, Fiona.'

Shivering, she sat up, pushing a hand through her hair to keep it back from her face. In the light her features were pinched and white, her lips bloodless.

'I thought I'd heard you,' he said conversationally, pushing the door closed behind him. He leaned back against it, arms folded. His expression was harsh and remote, blue eyes as cold as Arctic seas. 'I can see just what conclusions you've drawn, too.'

'Does it bother you?' she could not help asking bitterly.

'Not particularly. It might bother Denise, however.'

The girl's name made Fiona draw a hissing breath as she fought for control of her anger and black jealousy. 'And that would never do, would it?'

'Oh—for God's sake, Fiona——' he stopped, controlling himself with difficulty. 'Stop acting like a jealous wife,' he said icily. 'You have no right to behave like one, you know.'

She winced as though he had slapped her in the face. 'I'm sorry to sound like the dog in the manger. You're quite correct, of course. I have no right at all to resent any attentions you might pay to anyone. Especially not to Denise, who seems to feel that she has a few rights where you're concerned.'

'Poor Fiona,' he taunted, smiling savagely. 'Does it upset you to know that if you hadn't walked into my hotel room that day I might have married Denise? At least'—with a bitterness that roughed his voice into harshness—'I would have had a warm, passionate wife in my arms every night instead of being saddled with an icicle.'

The anger faded from her eyes, leaving them dead, almost unseeing. 'I can always go,' she said dully.

'Oh no.' Logan's expression was cruel, almost predatory as he came across the room to her. 'No, my dear. You're my wife, and Jonathan is my son. You stay here.'

Her mouth was parched, but she managed to say quickly, 'Don't you—don't you dare touch me!'

'Why? Does it repel you that my arms are still warm from Denise's, that her kiss is still on my mouth?' He laughed, and the savage mockery of it made her cower away from him, to try desperately to free herself from the hampering bedclothes so that she could run from this hateful room and the inhuman man who dominated it.

But she could not evade his arms or his mouth, and had to suffer the supreme humiliation of his kiss and the probing movements of his hands as he wrenched the front of her nightgown open and made himself conversant with every inch of her body, caressing her with lips and hands that every moment proved their experience.

Fiona turned her head into the pillow, fighting with clenched teeth the sensations that his savage but practised ardour gave her, fighting until her strength was gone and she lay spent, catching her breath in great sobbing gasps of fear and shame. Then he kissed her mouth once more, forcing it open beneath his before pushing her away and wiping his lips with the back of his hand.

'I'm not going to rape you,' he said in tones thick with disgust, eyes cold as they surveyed her nakedness. 'I must say, you've made a pretty good pretence at passion up until now. Stop looking like that—this is the last time I'll ever touch you, until you plead with me to do so.'

The drug she had taken made her eyes slumbrous and glazed beneath heavy half closed lids. His dark features, set in scorn and anger, wavered, doubled and then coalesced again. A sigh escaped her lips; without attempting to cover herself she turned her head into the pillow and closed her eyes.

'Fiona!'

His voice intruded through the welcoming blackness of sleep. With difficulty she opened her eyes again.

'Fiona, what did you take?'

The concerned tones made her smile faintly. 'Two—Ailsa's sleeping pills,' she murmured. 'Only two. I'm so tired.'

He said nothing further but pulled the bedclothes up to cover her. She sighed and put her hand out to touch his, whispering something, and then fell into the void, one cheek pillowed on her hand, sleeping as deeply as the child in the next room.

Logan sat staring down at her, his mouth twisted into an expression she had never seen, then he got up and switched the light off. The curtains billowed slightly as a breeze from the north crept in through the open window, but all else was silence and stillness.

A party at Whangatapu was a real social event for the whole district, and more than the family's reputation, for hospitality was at stake. Or so Jinny believed, if her feverish activity was anything to go by. Indeed, Fiona found herself with no time to think or plan in the next two days. Everyone got into the act, or was co-opted into it, even the Thurstons; Mrs Thurston proved a tower of strength when it came to scouring out the already immaculate house, and Forrest helped shift furniture and place the bowls of flowers Fiona arranged with her usual expertise.

Fiona liked him, but was afraid of those shrewd eyes

of his, especially when she and Logan were in the same room. It was quite easy for her husband to act as though there were no constraint between them, but try as she would to follow his lead she was well aware that Thurston knew something was wrong. He was even slightly protective towards her, and so, astonishingly enough, was his wife. At any other time this would have warmed Fiona's heart, but that organ seemed permanently frozen now.

Mary and Stephen arrived on Saturday morning just before lunch. Fiona found it easy to welcome them, easy to meet the curiosity in their eyes.

Mary was small and fair, pretty rather than beautiful, with exquisite skin and a too-sensitive mouth. Her husband seemed a less forceful copy of Logan, not quite so tall, slightly overweight, with eyes of the same blue which were just as implacable as his brother's. They behaved well, bringing with them what Mary called a belated wedding gift.

'Because I'll bet no one else has given you one,' she said merrily, 'and that seems an awful shame. I love looking at my wedding presents, even the hideous ones. Go on, open it.'

After a fleeting glance at Logan's withdrawn expression, Fiona did so, and gasped as the exquisite pottery figures were revealed. They formed a crêche, the Christ Child, His parents and the shepherds, the faithful animals portrayed in characteristic gestures, the sheep with its lamb suckling, the cow chewing, the donkey and horse with heads lifted alertly.

'It's beautiful,' Fiona breathed, a quick flush of colour staining her cheeks to sudden life. 'Thank you so much. Oh, Logan—look at the dog! It's just like Spray!'

Her fingers caressed the small figurines lovingly. No one could doubt her pleasure.

Thurston looked at his wife, who gave a tiny nod. With a muttered 'excuse me' he left the room, to reappear a few moments later carrying a square canvas.

'I know you said you didn't want her painted,' he observed, smiling at a suddenly grim Logan, 'but I'm afraid I'm quite unscrupulous when I've found a good subject. This was done from memory.'

It was a small canvas, but from it Fiona leapt into vivid life, Fiona wistful and triste, her fingers at a stylised keyboard, her clear eyes seeing things that Thurston's brushes had only hinted at.

'Fiona playing.' Thurston said firmly, putting the canvas up on to the mantel. 'When I have your permission, Logan, I'll do a proper portrait of her, because that's only a sketch of a mood.'

'You've caught it beautifully,' said Ailsa, breaking into what threatened to become an awkward silence. 'I've seen her like that often when she plays. What do you think of, Fiona, when you're at the piano?'

Fiona had not dared to look at Logan, in case she read anger in his expression, and she grasped at Ailsa's half-laughing question as though it was a lifeline.

'Great romantic dreams,' she said, smiling with a touch of mockery. 'I wallow in the music, which is why I'll never make a great player. Thank you, Forrest—I love it, but does my hair *really* have green lights in it?'

There was a general chuckle, Thurston accused her of being an artistic Philistine, and the moment was over. Logan added his thanks, and when Fiona went to lift the painting down told her to leave it there.

'You suit the room,' he said.

No one could have guessed the pain in Fiona's heart when she retorted cheerfully, 'I refuse to be part of the decor, Logan!'

'A very decorative part,' he said smoothly, 'and a permanent one. Leave it, Fiona. How about a companion piece, Forrest? Fiona laughing.'

'Are you commissioning my services?'

Logan smiled, and shook his head. 'You don't need my permission, apparently.'

'Well, I did try to capture her like that.' Thurston's eyes rested on Fiona's face with the peculiarly impersonal regard of the painter. 'It's much more difficult, actually. One always tends to caricature, when one paints mirth. And Fiona has that sparkle of mischief which is damned hard to capture without making her look as though she's telling a dirty joke. Still, one of these days I'll try it.' Laughter lit up the narrow eyes. '*With* your permission, Logan.'

After lunch everyone rested—the women, at least. Stephen and Logan went out for a look at the property; Fiona heard them go, discussing lambing percentages and the fertiliser requirements of volcanic country, and sighed as she turned away from the window. Tonight was going to be sheer hell, meeting all of the Sutherlands' friends as Logan's wife when things were so tense between them.

Impelled by an urgent need, she went into Jonathan's room. He slept peacefully in his bed, sprawled in the careless abandon of the very young, flushed and a little damp around the temples. When Fiona removed one of the blankets he stirred, then relaxed again. Her heart blocked her throat; she dropped on to the end of the bed, her hands up to her face. She could not leave him, could not cut herself off from him, even to ensure Logan's happiness. Shivering, she faced the prospect of life without Jonathan, empty beyond belief. To leave him would be like tearing her heart apart, and she was simply not strong enough to do it.

Great shudders racked her slender body as she fought a silent battle with herself. It left her weary and hopeless, no closer to a decision. At least she did not have to make up her mind immediately, for the shearers came on Monday, and Jinny could need her help until they left. It was a coward's way out, but it was respite of a sort.

Admit it, she told herself drearily, you don't want to go, and not just because you would have to leave the two people you love more than life itself. It was more than that. Softly, wary of disturbing the child in the bed, she got up and walked over to the window, gazing down at the emerald lawns and vivid flower beds, and beyond them the paddocks and the sea, glittering blue-green in the sunlight.

She had come to love Whangatapu, and to leave it, never to see it again, would add to the overwhelming grief she took with her. And the people, Ailsa, brisk yet oddly helpless, dour Jinny, her silent amiable husband, the Welsh family, the Sandersons—she had learned to like them all, to feel at ease with them. The whole way of life here was one she found intensely fulfilling.

Voices from below made her start and step back from the window. It was Logan and his brother on the terrace, back from their tour.

'... in good heart,' Stephen was saying. 'I got knocked with grass grub last summer, but the pasture seems to be coming away well now. By the way, I see you've resigned from the Board of Governors of the Pasture Institute. What made you do that? I thought it was one of your great interests.'

'Circumstances, the chief one being that I need to spend more time at home now.'

'Yes, I suppose so. I like your wife. *Not* what we expected at all.'

'Indeed?' Logan sounded forbidding. 'What did you expect?'

'Oh, nobody so poised and bright. Denise wrote to Mary that she was beautiful but had very little personality. Couldn't imagine you marrying a nobody, however beautiful; sounded like the old green eyes to me. I don't suppose Denise was at all pleased to find you had a wife tucked away all the time.'

'Denise has no reason to be jealous.' Logan's voice was coldly deliberate, like that of someone who is holding on to his temper with difficulty.

His brother laughed, apparently unimpressed. 'Oh, come now, Logan, don't try that on. Everyone expected you two to get married. She would have been ideal for you.'

'Everyone was wrong, then.'

'Are you trying to tell me that Denise knew all along that you had no intention of marrying her?'

Stephen sounded incredulous, as well he might, thought

Fiona bitterly. She could almost hear Logan shrug as he replied.

'I'm not trying to tell you anything, Steve. Leave it alone, will you? What happened between Denise and me is our business, no one else's.'

'If you say so. Myself, I'd say you got the better of the bargain. Denise is a nice kid, but she's a pretty ardent advocate of Denise Page. Your Fiona has something out of the ordinary, and she's obviously settled in well. I like the way she handles Mum. Nice nipper, too—a real Sutherland.'

Fiona walked away from the window, but she could hear Logan's voice warm with pride and affection as he spoke of his son. At least, she thought bleakly, she had given him something to be proud of, even if she had unwittingly taken his love from him. If he had to choose between Denise or Jonathan he would choose the child; had already done so when he married. It was his good fortune that his love was as accommodating as she was beautiful—and suitable.

CHAPTER NINE

THERE was a last-minute panic in the kitchen, but with Jinny in control it was nothing too devastating, so that Fiona had plenty of time to change before dinner. Jonathan came in to kiss her goodnight, and was suitably appreciative, hugging her fiercely.

Returning the hug with just as much strength, she rested her cheek on the damp hair, breathing in his little-boy smell, her heart a soggy mass of love. He was to eat in the kitchen with Jinny and Tom, and then Fiona would put him to bed well before any guests arrived, so that he would have time to get to sleep before the noisy part of the evening.

The door closed behind him, and she viewed herself gravely in the mirror, wondering just what Logan would think of her. The gown she had chosen was one he had not seen, a crêpe of soft grey, the colour of her eyes, halter-necked and backless, a slim, daring sheath which swirled in soft folds from her thighs to her feet. She had put her hair up in defiance of fashion, braiding it into a smooth roll at the back of her head. It made her neck swanlike, gave her poise and, she hoped, dignity. Not too much make-up, a touch of silvery-lilac eyeshadow, a pink lipstick, and colourless powder to prevent shine, for the night was warm.

For jewellery she had the rose diamond on her finger, and silver earrings which fell like twin waterfalls from the lobes of her ears. They were her mother's, dainty filigree work which came from Thailand and gave her face an exotic Eastern look.

Slowly she touched perfume to her wrists and throat, replaced the bottle and turned to greet Logan as he came in through the bathroom door.

He looked quite magnificent in evening clothes, tall and

sternly handsome, exuding the arrogant self-confidence which made him seem almost overpowering to her heightened nerves.

'Are you ready?' he asked.

'As you see.'

'Then do up these damned cufflinks, will you?'

She laughed, suddenly at ease. Like a modern god he might look, but cufflinks, it seemed, reduced all men to the same level. She could remember that exact intonation in her father's voice before an evening out!

The cufflinks were greenstone set in silver, tricky to manipulate, but she fitted them into place with steady fingers, refusing to allow his nearness to disturb her.

'Thank you,' he said briefly when she had finished. 'Let's go.'

As she turned away she thought wryly that it was just as well she hadn't hoped for compliments, because it was clear that the state of armed truce between them was not going to be replaced by anything warmer. Nevertheless the frozen feeling around her heart melted slightly when he asked quietly, 'Are you nervous, Fiona?'

'Yes,' she admitted.

'Don't be. I won't be far from you, and everyone will be disposed to be friendly, even those who are curious.' He sent her a slanting, narrowed-eyed glance. 'Be prepared for open mouths at first. You've certainly set out to lay them in the aisles, haven't you?'

'Yes,' she said baldly.

A smile curved his mouth. 'You've succeeded.'

They said nothing else all the way down the stairs, but those few words helped her. Logan poured sherry for them both in the big, empty drawing-room, and when the rest of the family came in, more or less together, they must have seemed a perfectly normal couple, talking quietly together in the french doors overlooking the terrace as the sun caught and gilded their silhouettes.

Two hours later Fiona was exhilarated by the knowledge that this, her first party, possessed that indefinable something which would set it apart from all other occasions. It could have been the fact that most of those there knew each other well, or perhaps it was the superb setting and the delight that comes from wearing one's best clothes, but wherever her eyes fell her guests were talking and laughing, obviously having a wonderful time.

Mary was holding court amongst a circle of women, extremely attractive in pale blue and without that constrained look she had worn up until now, as if she had to guard every word she said. Fiona's eyes roamed the room to find Stephen, a slight frown between her brows. Yes, there he was, and there was yet another full glass in his hand. That made the fourth she had seen there. Still, apart from a slight flush, he seemed perfectly sober, talking to a middle-aged couple. Logan was circulating at the moment, making sure that everyone was looked after, while his mother was seated on a sofa talking with animation to a tall gentleman—Bob Standish—from further up the coast. Denise's parents seemed perfectly happy, with a group of people their own age.

Fiona watched Mrs Page for a moment. She was a thin, beautifully dressed woman with fashionably frosted hair and for a time she had looked exhausted. She had recovered now, however, judging by her air of gaiety, although her husband's hand was protective at her elbow.

And Denise? Stunning in old gold chiffon, she was flirting simultaneously with three men, one of whom was Danny Harmon. As Fiona's gaze slid past the group he lifted his lashes and looked at her. Something unspoken quivered in the air between them, then he began to move purposefully towards her through the crowd.

Damn, Fiona thought, but she did not move. There was little of a personal nature he could say here, surrounded by so many people, but in spite of her sympathy for him he made her uneasy, and she would have chosen not to speak to him.

'Hi,' he said softly as he came up to her. 'All alone? Where's that husband of yours?'

'He's busy.'

'Ah yes, the perfect host. As you are the perfect hostess. Having fun?'

Fiona considered. 'Not really, not having fun, but I am enjoying myself. Like the way a conductor must enjoy himself, when the orchestra produces beautiful music because of him.'

He chuckled, his expression alive with interest. 'I know exactly what you mean, and you make a very good executive director. Everyone is having a whale of a time, and I can promise you they'll still be remembering it six months from now. May I tell you how fabulous you look?'

A slight flush touched her cheeks, for there was a sort of yearning in his tone which belied the mockery of his glance. 'Yes, of course,' she said lightly. 'I think we all do, don't you? What you might call an elegant assembly of beautiful people. Who is the little dark woman over there in the corner, Danny? She looks a bit bewildered.'

'Sonia Raintree. That's her husband flirting so ardently with Denise, the big blond chap. If his wife stripped naked in the middle of the floor I doubt if he'd notice.'

'Poor girl.' Fiona gave an anxious look around, but there was no member of the family heading for Mrs Raintree with rescue in their eyes. 'I'll have to go and talk to her, Danny. She looks lost.'

'I'll come with you. Between us, we might lighten that frozen expression.'

Within five minutes he had Sonia Raintree laughing, to reveal that beneath what he called her frozen expression was a face of little beauty but considerable charm.

After a few more minutes Fiona excused herself, and set off across the room. She and Logan met halfway, he holding a glass.

'Have something to drink,' he said in her ear. 'You must be thirsty.'

'It is hot, isn't it?' Gratefully accepting the glass she took a small sip of the contents. 'What is it? It's beautiful.'

'Champagne cup. Don't drink it too fast, or I'll have to carry you upstairs.'

To any onlookers they must look a devoted couple, she thought calmly. Logan was smiling down at her; no one but she could see that the warmth of that smile failed to reach his eyes.

'I'll drink it very slowly,' she promised, smiling up into his eyes as if he were the love and light of her life. 'Everything seems to be going well. Shall I put the record player on?'

'Yes, it's time, but I'll do it.'

Most of the younger people, and quite a few of the older, found the lure of moonlight and dancing too much to resist. Soon after the soft strains of the orchestra began to beguile the air the crowd in the room had thinned out considerably. Fiona, talking to Sylvia Bond, one of the Play Centre mothers, resplendent in dark red which suited her slightly matronly figure, saw Denise talking to Logan at the french windows, her vivid face upturned like a flower to his. She seemed to be asking something, something Logan refused, for she pouted at his answer and turned to meet Fiona's eyes.

Sudden malice glittered in the dark glance; Denise gave a long slow smile to her hostess, said something to Logan and allowed herself to be led off by the Raintree man who had been standing to one side.

With difficulty, shaken by the brazen defiance of Denise's stare, Fiona dragged her attention back to her companion.

'... marvellous,' Sylvia was finishing enthusiastically. 'You must come and see me some time before very long. After all, we are only seven miles down the road.'

'I'd love to,' Fiona returned. 'Ailsa tells me you have a loom, and that you can't produce enough weaving for the demand.'

Sylvia blushed slightly. 'Well—yes,' she admitted. 'It started as a hobby, but the terrific upsurge in arts and crafts has meant that there's a big market for the sort of stuff I do.' She smiled over Fiona's shoulder. 'Hullo,

Logan, I'm just congratulating your wife on the fabulous party.'

'I'm glad you're enjoying yourself,' Logan said smoothly, dropping a possessive arm over Fiona's shoulders. 'Where's Kevin?'

'Talking sheep,' his loving wife returned with a grin which made her look very much younger. 'No, I malign him. Here he comes.'

For a few moments they all four stayed chatting, then Logan excused himself and Fiona, sweeping her off to dance with him with the cool mastery she found so attractive—and irritating.

He was, of course, a superb dancer. It was many years since Fiona had danced, but she found her steps matching his perfectly, and after a moment relaxed in his arms, content for even a few moments to allow him supreme control of her actions.

They had never talked much while dancing. Logan, she remembered wistfully, used to say that it disturbed his concentration. It had been one of the little things that made him so unique to her. Now, his hand moved gently across the silken skin of her back as though he loved the feel of it and he said below his breath, 'I'd better not see anyone else touching you like this.'

For answer she smiled brilliantly at him and linked her arms around his neck, swaying provocatively against him in as sensuous a manner as she could manage.

On a sharp indrawn breath he muttered, 'Behave yourself, Fiona!'

Recklessly consumed by a mad desire to anger him, she retorted, 'Why? I'm your wife, remember? Everyone here assumes that our marriage is entirely normal—as you've made sure they should. What's unusual about a wife flirting with her husband at a party?'

'Nothing, except that you're not behaving like a wife, my dear. You're flaunting yourself like a woman set on seduction.'

She laughed, but warned by the gleam of anger in his

stabbing glance, loosed her hands and resumed the more conventional embrace, aware that she had irrevocably lost any chance of making their marriage a normal one. Her blatant attempt at stirring his senses had only roused his contempt.

Quite rightly, she thought bitterly. She had had her chance and had blown it because of an arrogant desire to have him love her. She should have been content with what he had to offer, not gone crying for the moon. Now she had lost everything. She looked up and found the colour hot on her cheeks at the lazy penetrating glance.

'What's so interesting?' she asked quietly.

'You are. I'll bet you're the only wife in the room who blushes when her husband looks at her.'

'Well, don't!' she retorted crossly. 'Logan, who is Bob Standish?'

A mocking smile partly answered the intention behind the question. 'A very old, very devoted friend of Mother's. At one time I hoped that they'd marry, but she seems content with friendship. Thinking of trying your hand at a little matchmaking? Take my advice and leave them alone. They're both mature people, well able to run their own lives.'

'And that's put me in my place,' she murmured.

'Only you can do that.'

The flush on her cheeks deepened, but she met the full impact of his derisory glance with candid eyes.

'Logan——' she stopped, hesitating.

'Mm?'

'Oh, it doesn't matter.'

He nodded. 'Hardly the time or the place, is it? Fiona, where did you learn to dance so well? You're like thistledown on your feet.'

'You taught me, remember?'

'Yes, I remember. I wondered if you did. Do you remember the first time we met?'

'When I fell at your feet?' She smiled rather wistfully. 'It was rather appropriate, wasn't it?'

'Perhaps. I had no defences either, you know. It was the first time I'd ever lost my head completely. You were so beautiful and innocent and you gave yourself with quite terrifying intensity. I tried to track you down after you left, but had no luck. Then my father died, and I had to go back.'

'Your father's death must have been a great shock,' she said soberly. 'It was totally unexpected, wasn't it?'

'Yes. Do you understand what I'm trying to explain, Fiona?'

She reacted to the impatience in his voice with that fleeting touch of mischief which made her intensely provocative. 'Yes, but you needn't apologise for what happened so long ago, Logan. Innocent though I was I knew that I wasn't the first woman you'd made love to. You were far too good at it.'

His hand tightened across her back. 'So you thought me a careless philanderer, and that was that!'

Suddenly it seemed important to disabuse his mind of this notion. 'Oh, Logan—no! Like you, I lost my head completely, and how could I blame you for taking what I offered so eagerly? I didn't—I don't. I never could. After all, Jonathan came of it.'

'Yes.' He was silent for a few moments, then said unexpectedly, 'I'd like to have met your parents.'

'They were darlings,' she murmured. 'Practical and gentle—I think they must have wondered whether they had a cuckoo in the nest when I arrived on the scene, but they were always loving and very understanding. I think you would have liked them, Logan. They adored Jonathan.'

'In common with almost everyone else,' he said wryly. 'Charm is a very potent weapon.'

She laughed up at him. 'You should know, you have swags of it, most unfairly.'

He made a masculine grimace at this, then the music stopped, and with his arm around her he took her across the floor to where Mary and her partner stood.

Mary looked pale, as though she had a headache. Fiona

murmured a remark about the heat, and suggested something to drink.

'Mm, lovely,' Mary responded eagerly. 'Just lime juice for me, Logan. I've had enough champagne cup already.'

The two men went off upon this errand of mercy, leaving Fiona with Mary, alone on the crowded terrace.

'Let's sit down,' said Fiona. 'I don't know about you, but my feet are killing me, and Ailsa seems to be in charge again.'

'Has she dismissed the faithful Bob?' Mary gave a sigh of relief as they sat down on the sofa against the study windows. 'Oh, this is good! I don't need to tell you what a howling success this party is, Fiona.'

'No, it is going well, and I'm so pleased. I've had the most appalling butterflies for weeks at the thought of it, but I should have known that with Jinny and Logan in charge nothing could go wrong.'

'You too,' her companion said generously. 'You've done well. Fiona—I know this isn't the time or place, but there are a few things I want to say to you.'

There was an empty gap in Fiona's stomach, but she braced herself. The last thing she wanted was a heart-to-heart chat with Mary; it was inevitable, however, she could see that after one glance at the determination on the pretty face.

'Fire ahead,' she said.

'About Logan and me. There was nothing in it. I lost my head for a while, but it was always Stephen for me, although it took Logan at his most brutal to show me that. Only Danny won't believe that. He wants Denise, and he's jealous because she won't have anything to do with him. He—he wants to make trouble, and I can't make him see that—oh, well, I don't suppose it matters overmuch.'

The wide eyes were shadowed and lacklustre as they gazed appealingly at Fiona. 'You seem happy enough together. I noticed you watching Steve and me. He doesn't understand. I thought that by marrying him I was showing him who I loved, but it hasn't quite worked out that way.'

She tried to smile. 'Most of the time we rub along together very well, you know.'

Fiona's heart moved with compassion. 'I think you're very courageous,' she said gently, laying her hand over the small one that gripped a fine handkerchief so tightly. It moved convulsively under hers, then clung fiercely for a moment, and fell away as Danny came up.

'I think Logan is lucky,' Mary said softly, before tossing a laughing greeting to her brother.

He replied in kind, his expression alert, almost predatory as he pulled up a chair beside Fiona.

'The two most beautiful girls in the whole place, and no male to keep them company,' he said extravagantly. 'Your husbands don't deserve you, my loves.'

The meaning in his voice was plain, but Fiona ignored it. 'What husband ever does?' she demanded cheerfully.

'Aha—a Women's Libber in our midst! I wonder if Logan knows?'

'If Logan knows what?' He handed Mary her glass, then one to Fiona, and stood regarding Danny with a smile.

Danny returned it; to all outward appearances they were exchanging pleasantries, but the tension crackled between them, tangible, threatening. Mary made a sudden movement, then drank half of the lime juice, as Danny retorted, 'Your wife has just proved herself a fan of Women's Liberation. Did you know you were nourishing a snake in your bosom, Logan?'

'Of course.' He rested a hand on her bare shoulder, the man in possession. 'You must admit she's a good advertisement for them.'

'Oh, to be sure.' Danny jumped up, made an elaborate bow. 'So much so that I must ask her to dance. Have I your permission, Logan?'

It was a direct challenge. Fiona felt an increased pressure of the hand that rested on her shoulder, but Logan merely said mildly, 'She doesn't need my permission to dance, Danny.'

'Then, beautiful Mrs Logan, come and dance with me. You can safely leave Mary with Logan now.'

Fiona bit her lip, but got up to go with him, saying severely once they were out of earshot, 'Do you enjoy embarrassing your sister?'

He looked shamefaced. 'No, it was rotten of me. I'll apologise.'

'Better leave it alone,' she advised crisply. 'Just don't do it again.'

Heaving an elaborate sigh, he drew her into his arms. 'Now I've made you cross with me, and I was going to behave so beautifully. Hey, relax, I'm not going to bite you.'

'You're holding me too close.'

He laughed, and loosened his grip, gazing down at her with teasing lights in his eyes. 'O.K., I'll be very good, but you make it hard for a chap, you know. That dress is just made for dalliance on the dance floor.'

He still held her too closely, but he did behave himself, setting out to beguile himself back into her good books. He succeeded so well that before long she was laughing and relaxed with him; to her surprise she found him an extremely entertaining companion.

After that the evening flew. Most of the older people left soon after supper, but the younger ones determined to make a night of it, and at three o'clock they were all on the beach singing round a bonfire to the music of a guitar.

Fiona was thoroughly enjoying herself, seated between Logan and Danny, when the guitarist said, 'Here, I've run out of steam. Can you play, Fiona?'

She was taken aback, but accepted the instrument. Logan removed his arm from around her and said lazily, 'Go ahead, Fiona.'

It was a good guitar, mellow and well cared for. She strummed for a few moments, then launched into a Maori love song, *Pokare kare Ana*, a plaintively beautiful tune about star-crossed lovers. Everyone joined in; when they finished she gave them a medley of pops and folk songs which kept them singing for over half an hour, before she looked around, saw several yawns, and started on *Now is the Hour*, that haunting song of farewell. There was a general chuckle, but everyone joined in, and that was the end of the party. The men doused the fire as the women collected their things, there was a general farewell amid thanks and congratulations, and, tired out, Fiona began to collect glasses from all around the house and stack them in the dishwasher, while Logan took Denise home as her parents had left some hours before.

That hurt, but Fiona put aside the ferocious jealousy that threatened to devour her as she moved quietly around, emptying ashtrays, purposefully filling in time.

On the third trip back to the kitchen she found Stephen there, sitting at the big table with his head resting on his hands. As she came in he lifted his head, gave her a crooked smile and said, 'The perfect housewife. Or are you waiting up to see how long it takes Logan to see Denise home?'

He was not drunk, but he had had more than was good for him. 'My wife hates Denise,' he went on broodingly before Fiona could speak. 'She hates you, too.'

'Do you think so?' Fiona was surprised. 'Oh, I don't think so. I hope she doesn't, as it will make things very awkward.'

He gave her a slightly owlish stare. 'Cool customer, aren't you? I've been wondering what Logan sees in you beside your looks. Perhaps it's that unapproachable air—he's always liked a challenge, my big brother, and I must say you present one. As for Mary—oh yes, she hates you. You got Logan, you see. She still wants him. Little brother isn't good enough.' He gave a heavy maudlin sigh. 'I've been watching her, all these years. 'S funny—I watch her, she watches Logan, Logan watches you, and you—you sit like a little cat and watch nothing, unless it's the boy. I don't like watching Mary hurt herself. I love Mary.'

'Do you?' Fiona was not sure if the tactics she was about

to use were the best, but she went ahead just the same. 'I thought it was deliberate.'

'Deliberate? What's deliberate?'

'The way you force her on the defensive all the time.'

Bewilderment fought with truculence in his expression. Truculence won. 'What the hell do you mean?'

'Well, you're so very conscious of Logan's presence that you force her to be. I don't know her very well, but I'm a woman, and that's humiliation. And your attitude must reinforce it a thousandfold. No wonder she gets jittery when she sees you watching her. I'm sure she thinks you enjoy putting her through the hoops, but if you love her . . .'

She allowed her voice to trail off, casually shrugging her shoulders.

'I do,' he said bleakly, and beneath the slightly drunken aggression she had a glimpse of the pain and frustration that were his ever-present companions.

Compassion was not in order, however. Hardening her heart, she returned casually, 'Then your desire for revenge must be greater than your love, or you're very stupid. It's a wonder she hasn't left you. I think she must love you very much to stick it out.'

'She loves Logan,' he stated stubbornly, as if he couldn't face the implications of her remarks.

'Then she's a masochist,' Fiona said firmly, setting a mug of black coffee before him. 'She would have to be, to enjoy the situation she's in. She looks unhappy to me, however.'

Automatically Stephen drank, then put the mug down, frowning at it as though he had never seen coffee before.

'If she loved me she would show it,' he said slowly, one lean finger tracing the raised pattern on the side of the mug.

'I don't suppose she gets much encouragement,' Fiona returned mildly. 'What do you expect her to do? Would you believe her if she told you she loved you?'

'I——' He looked up, his expression arrested, then with

a quick shake of his head, 'No, why should I?'

'Why indeed? I suppose you expect her to make some grand gesture to prove it to you?' She smiled mockingly. 'It's rather hard these days to die of love, and there's not much else she can do except stick to you in spite of everything.'

There was a long silence. Then he drank the rest of the coffee, and set the mug down on the bench, saying heavily, 'Why do you bother yourself about us? You don't even know us.'

'Because,' she said, choosing her words with care, 'it irritates me to see two people who are besotted with each other tearing themselves apart and making everyone uncomfortable. And if you don't realise that she loves you, brother-in-law, you're so insensitive that you don't deserve her—or the baby.'

This was a calculated and deliberate ploy; mentally she prayed that Mary would forgive her for revealing the truth of her condition.

Stephen stared, the ruddy flush paling in his cheeks. 'What—what did you say?'

'You heard. I didn't think she had told anyone yet, but the minute I saw her I knew she was pregnant.'

White-faced, suddenly far older-looking, he shook his head at her. 'I—she—*why* hasn't she told me? She knows that I—that I ...'

'Would accuse Logan of fathering it?' Fiona supplied brutally, pressing her point home with sledgehammer force.

A dull flush mottled his cheeks. To her dismay tears came to his eyes; he swallowed, then said grittily, 'I've never accused her of—of being unfaithful. *Never!*'

'Not in words, perhaps,' said Fiona, suddenly liking him very much. 'It's fairly implicit in your attitude.'

'Oh, my God!' he whispered. He dropped his forehead on his hand, stayed like that while she washed the mug and put it away, then said with a dignity she had not thought he possessed, 'You hit damned hard, little cat.

That's what you remind me of, the cat that walked by itself, all cool and amused. Well, what do I do now? You seem to know everything—tell me that.'

'Just trust her—and show it,' Fiona said gently. 'She's proud too—you Sutherlands haven't got a monopoly on that quality, you know. Don't let her realise that you know about the baby, she'll want to tell you herself. For heaven's sake, man, I don't have to tell you how to treat your wife! You've known all along how to make her happy, or you wouldn't have done such a good job of making her unhappy!'

Stephen winced at that, but caught her by the elbow as she moved past him, his eyes almost pleading as he asked: 'She'll wonder what the hell has got into me if I change so suddenly.'

Fiona gave him her very sweet, slightly mischievous smile. 'Perhaps, but I'd bet she'll be so grateful that she won't enquire too deeply. I doubt if she'll want any reasons.'

He laughed then, and stood up, catching her across the shoulders in a warm hug. 'I think my brother got more than he bargained for when he snared you, little cat who walks by herself. Denise said you were a nonentity—I'd love to see her face when she realises how very wrong she is.'

'Well, that day may never come,' Fiona retorted, releasing herself.

He looked down at her, slim and small and yet packing such a punch. With sudden worry in the blue eyes so like Logan's he said, 'Perhaps, but——'

'There's no need to worry, Stephen,' she told him firmly. 'Off you go. Good luck.'

Still slightly perturbed, he smiled and said meaningly, 'Good luck to you, too. And I mean that.'

'Luck doesn't come into it, Stephen.' She did not say it aloud, however. If she had managed to make him see his marriage in a new light then she had done some good in her stay here; perhaps Logan would think kindly of her for that, if he ever knew. She went on with her work, and before long had the rooms tidy, the windows open to let in fresh air, but Logan had still not come home.

Wearily she climbed the stairs, took off the lovely grey gown and hung it up, creamed her face clean and climbed into bed as the first cockerel heralded the coming dawn.

CHAPTER TEN

For someone who had little or no sleep the night before Logan appeared incredibly fresh to Fiona's jaundiced eyes.

'Wake up,' he said, ruthlessly shaking her shoulder. 'It's ten o'clock, Fiona; your son has something to show you.'

Heavy with sleep, slightly headachy, she put a hand to her yawning lips, muttering, 'Why don't you just drop dead or something!' then gasping, 'Ten o'clock! It *can't* be! I set the alarm for seven.'

'I turned it off when I got in,' he told her, sitting on the edge of the bed to watch her with unkind eyes as she pushed the heavy hair back from her cheeks. 'You were sleeping so soundly that you didn't even stir when I came in.'

For a moment Fiona was bewildered under his mocking gaze, then as realisation flooded over her she turned her head to see the dented pillow and crumpled bedclothes on the other side of the bed.

'That was hardly necessary, surely,' she said stiffly.

He shrugged. 'With guests in the house I'm taking no chances. You didn't seem to object, anyway. Or do you usually cuddle up to whoever happens to climb into bed with you? Fiona asleep is much more approachable than Fiona awake.'

'What——' she stopped, scarlet with shame and embarrassment. Surely he had not had the audacity to come to her warm from Denise's embrace and steal what she would not willingly give?

'Relax,' he said smoothly, 'I was too tired to respond to your open invitation. Although——' with a drawl that made her want to hit him, 'I could summon up the energy now, if you're still in the same mood. That nightgown reeals far more than it conceals. Very fetching and provocative.'

'Oh—go and jump in the lake!' she flared, furious with herself for allowing him the power to arouse her every nerve to tingling life.

He captured her hands and drew her into the circle of his arms, looking down at her mutinous face with a quirk of humour.

'No, don't erupt just yet, fireball. You have too much to do for a display of temperament. Jonathan and I are going to give you exactly half an hour to get up and have some breakfast, before we drag you off to the horse paddock. The shearers come tomorrow, which means a vast baking for you and Jinny this afternoon. The Thurstons are leaving and Denise is coming over to give you a hand.' He felt her stiffen, and murmured cruelly, 'So you'll be able to see whether I made love to her last night, as you have such a discerning eye for my peccadilloes.'

Just what she would have said—or done—at this juncture Fiona never knew; all of her being was caught up in a white blaze of rage when they were interrupted by a knock at the door, and the whirlwind entrance of Mary, radiant in a white fluffy housecoat. Fiona took one astounded look at her and wondered why on earth she had ever thought her just pretty, for this girl was beautiful!

'Am I interrupting something?' she almost babbled as she flew across the room. 'Well, I don't care if I am. Fiona, you darling, darling girl! I love you, love you, love you, and if there's ever anything I can do for you I'll do it gladly even if it means selling my engagement ring.' She flung tempestuous arms around them both, for Fiona was still locked in Logan's embrace, kissed Fiona, then Logan, laughed, and blushed, and sat down abruptly on the side of the bed, the tears coming to her eyes as she looked at their bewilderment.

'You *do* look funny, both of you! No, Logan, I haven't gone mad, or only with joy. Ask Fiona about it—she'll tell you. Fiona, Steve and I had a long talk last night, when he came up, and I think we've cleared everything up, and it was all because of you, you wonderful, sensible, tough minded thing! So I told him about the baby—you're going to be an uncle in six months' time, Logan—and if it's a girl I'm going to call it after you, Fiona. And I'm so happy I *could* cry!'

'Not here!' Fiona said cheerfully, delighted that her few words had borne such fruit. She fought down a pang of envy. Mary and Stephen deserved this joy, after the years of stubborn pride and misunderstanding. 'You know what men are like when women cry,' she went on. 'You would embarrass poor Logan horribly.'

'Poor Logan nothing!' Mary blew her nose, then tucked the handkerchief back into her pocket. 'Logan is quite un-embarrassable.'

And she left them, borne so lightly in her happiness that her feet barely skimmed the floor. Logan waited until the door shut behind her before looking down into his wife's face. 'Envy, Fiona? It doesn't suit you. How did you do it?'

'Just a little plain speaking.' She moved in his arms, trying to free herself, but he tightened his hold painfully.

'No—stay there. You wouldn't by any chance be thinking of leaving Whangatapu, would you?'

During the short silence that followed his inspired guess she fought desperately for words to allay his suspicions. None came, and she knew that she looked a perfect example of guilt. His expression hardened into ruthlessness.

'So I was right. Fiona, if you try to leave here I'll follow you and when I catch up with you I'll make you wish you'd never been born. I mean it!'

Further concealment was useless. Nervously she had to lick her lips before she asked in a voice little more than a whisper, 'How did you know?'

There was no sign of softening in the rigid lines and planes of his face. Never had he looked more cruelly purposeful. 'I can read you like a book, my dear. You little fool, do you think I'm blind?'

His hands on her upper arms relaxed as he pushed her away. 'We can't talk now, but until we can, remember one thing. You are not leaving Whangatapu no matter what happens, no matter what justification you've dreamed up in that woolly mind of yours for such a step. You made your bed when you agreed to marry me, and no matter how painful the lying in it, you'll have to learn to live with it.'

'You didn't tell me about Denise, or I might not have married you,' she choked, goaded beyond discretion by his cold harshness.

'There was nothing to tell,' he said implacably. 'Nothing.'

'Logan—I——'

'Fiona, if you'd trusted me for your own sake as much as you did for Jonathan's, you would never have backed yourself into the corner you find yourself in now. I hoped you would, but the trust has always been all on my side. Until you make up your mind to trust me, we go on the way we are now. Now, will you get up, or do you want to keep Jonathan waiting?'

'No—at least——' she paused, but he made no move to get up from the bed. 'Logan, will you go away?'

'No,' he retorted implacably. 'You're my wife, and I have every right to stay in your bedroom while you get changed.'

Casting him a furious glance, she flung back the bedclothes, climbed out of bed and shrugged herself into her housecoat, tying the ribbons across it with vicious little jerks. He grinned, taunting her, as she took out underclothes and jeans, a sweater and blouse before marching into the bathroom and closing the door behind her with a defiant click. With her mind a turmoil of worry and indecision she washed, dressed herself and combed her hair, then swept back into the bedroom.

Logan was standing by the dressing table, looking at the photograph of her parents. He did not turn as she came in, so that all she saw was his profile, the high brow, the arrogant line of nose, the firmness of his mouth and chin. A wave of love and desire so intense that it made her tremble swept over her, and she said blindly, 'Logan——'

'Ah, you're ready. Come on, then. Your son is trying to contain his impatience in the kitchen, and has probably driven Jinny mad.'

And so the moment passed, and she went with him down the stairs and out into the greyness of the day outside.

They were all there, even Ailsa, who admitted to a slight headache but seemed far more relaxed than she had ever been before. Relaxed was perhaps the wrong word, Fiona thought, wondering. Perhaps she was happy because Stephen and Mary were so obviously happy. Ailsa had never struck her as being particularly maternal, but the situation between her second son and his wife must have worried her. And this gave rise to another less pleasant train of thought. Perhaps Ailsa worried too about Logan's marriage. Except that she and Logan always appeared in public to be—well, friendly. She hoped!

The sun came out as they reached the horse paddock, gilding the hills and the flat, working its magic on the harbour to change it from sullen grey to a blue that sparkled.

'Summer's nearly here,' Mary said idly. 'You'll notice the heat, Fiona.'

Jinny nodded. 'I must order the geese from Smiths for Christmas,' she said. 'Or would you prefer turkeys, Fiona? Geese might be too rich for Jonathan.'

There was a general chuckle, in which she joined after a moment. 'You know I see the world from my kitchen,' she defended herself cheerfully. 'After shearing, Fiona, we'll have to get together about Christmas.'

'You'll really enjoy it, Fiona,' Mary told her enthusiastically. 'Logan always puts on a huge barbecue for everyone on Christmas Eve; everybody has a candle and we sing all the traditional carols. The kids love it, especially when the presents are given out. It's really patriarchal!'

Logan laughed, put his hand under Fiona's elbow and reached a hand down to Jonathan, who was fairly buzzing with impatience at their leisurely pace across the grass.

'And you, my love, will have to buy the presents this year. I'm quite sure Mother will give up the task with real gratitude.'

'Indeed *yes*!' Ailsa said fervently.

There was more laughter, so that Danny, lounging against the white rails of the horse paddock, saw a cheerful group coming up to him. His eyes flickered immediately to his sister's face, then with dawning wonder, to Stephen's. Both were totally relaxed, free from any form of tension; as he watched, Stephen hugged Mary and dropped a kiss on her brow. Comprehension gave Danny's expression a comical bewilderment, then he smiled, sighed, and turned away as though their patent happiness hurt him.

The Welsh family was waiting, too. After the greetings Jonathan hopped through the rails, took a carrot from his pocket, and called, his clear treble tossed across the grass by a wayward little wind from the sea. A neat chestnut pony came across, mane and tail flying. Fiona watched, unaware that she was gripping Logan's arm so tightly that her nails were marking the skin.

'Relax,' he said, in a voice pitched only for her ear. 'He's done it all before.'

And indeed, as the pony bent to take the carrot, Jonathan grabbed the mane, talking softly, and slipped the bridle on. Janey Welsh helped with the saddle, but Jonathan, looking so serious that Fiona's heart contracted, checked all of the bits and pieces that were apparently vital, and then led the pony across to the stump of an old tree. A moment, and he was sitting proudly in the saddle, feet tucked into the stirrups, hands holding the bridle carefully and correctly.

The Welsh boys cheered loudly, setting the pony to tossing its head, but Jonathan was fully in control, and without a glance at his audience, set about showing off his accomplishments. The pony, whose name, Fiona discovered, was Flinders, walked, trotted, cantered back and forth in front of them, obedient to Jonathan's hands on the reins. At least, Fiona presumed that was how he did it. To her it looked like magic.

Then, still oblivious of them all, he went through the whole process in reverse, but when saddle and bridle had been removed Flinders followed Jonathan up to the fence, nuzzling the scarlet jersey with what seemed real affection.

Only when he reached his mother did he look up, and allow himself to smile, a great grin that nearly split his face in two.

Fiona's throat clogged. She swallowed twice, then said, 'Darling, that was terribly good! You're an excellent pupil!'

'You won't worry about me when I ride now,' he said, then stopped being the serious equestrian and climbed through the rails and buried his head in her waist, clinging fiercely with his strong young arms.

'I never worried, silly old thing,' Fiona said tenderly, cuddling him close to her. 'I knew you'd be safe with Daddy. Hey, cut it out, boy, your jockey cap is digging into my tummy!'

A muffled chuckle, and then he looked up, his face rosy with mischief. 'Now you've seen how easy it is, you can learn too,' he teased.

Fiona swallowed again. 'Ah—yes, I suppose so,' she returned faintly. She looked up, caught a glimmer of—something—in Logan's expression. The words he had said so bitterly only a few minutes ago came to mind. 'If only you trusted me for your own sake as much as you do for Jonathan,' he had said, and she knew what she had to say.

'Never let it be said that my son can do something I can't,' she said strongly. 'Darling, both you and Daddy can teach me, and I bet I'll turn out a better rider than either of you.'

Jonathan gave a crow of triumph, but Logan had turned away so that she could not see how he reacted to her announcement. Now he turned back, but there was nothing but conventional pleasure in his voice as he said, 'Good girl. We'll work her until she drops, won't we, Jonno?'

So Fiona was denied any gratification, any hint that her overture had been noticed or valued. Still, through the rest of the day she felt oddly buoyed up, as though an important decision had been made, one that would change her life.

Mary and Stephen left after lunch, waving effusive goodbyes, and shortly after them the Thurstons, who had decided to go when they heard of the shearers' arrival.

'Because you've never had to cope with them before,' said Mrs Thurston placidly, 'but you'll find yourself run off your feet, my dear. They eat like horses! And you won't want visitors cluttering up the place.'

Just before they left Forrest reminded his host of his desire to paint Fiona. Logan was noncommittal, but he did promise to get in touch with the artist if he changed his mind, and with that Forrest had to be content.

It was quite the busiest afternoon Fiona had ever spent. Jinny was working at top speed, baking vast quantities of pies and bread simultaneously, ready for the shearers. Fiona helped her, glad to do something which took her mind off herself, and when Denise arrived, svelte and very satisfied, she was wrapping things in plastic film to take out to the freezer room. Denise was an extremely efficient worker, and between them they stacked a couple of shelves high with food, before Jinny gave them a cup of tea and shooed them, none too politely, out.

At some stage of the afternoon the shearing gang had arrived and were now settling into their quarters. They had a cook of their own, but apparently the homestead helped out as much as they could with food.

'Let's go into the morning room, shall we?' Denise suggested brightly, for all the world as though it was she, and not Fiona, who was mistress here.

Fiona felt her hackles rise, but subdued them. Life was complicated enough without getting angry at Denise, who would find a malicious pleasure in making sure Logan heard of it! So she acquiesced calmly, and was aware immediately that something was going to happen, that Denise was preparing herself for a confrontation of sorts. Her whole mind rejected the idea. Tired after last night and the hectic afternoon, she simply could not be bothered exchanging malicious pleasantries with this girl who was doing her level best to undermine her life.

There was, however, to be no escape. Jonathan and Logan were over with the shearers, Ailsa was upstairs in her bedroom, resting, probably sleeping; and Jinny would be no help.

So, resigning herself, Fiona went into the morning room, so-called because it faced east and caught the morning sun. Now it was cool and shaded, the only vivid colour a bowl of rosy Sweet Williams. The cottagey flowers suited the room, diffusing a faint scent on the air like a remembrance of spring.

For once Denise seemed ill at ease. She prowled around the room, staring at the objects in it without the usual gleam of possessiveness in her eyes, before turning to face Fiona, by now seated in a comfortable armchair.

'I think it's about time we had the gloves off,' she said abruptly.

Sudden laughter glinted in Fiona's face. 'Not if you're going to talk in clichés,' she returned amiably.

The red lips tightened into a thin straight line. Denise hated being laughed at. 'Don't be so damned insolent,' she said roughly, then caught herself up. 'Don't you think it's about time you left here?' she said coldly. 'There's nothing to keep you any longer. Jonathan is well settled in, and I promise you that I'll take good care of him. I know that that's what's worrying you.'

Oddly enough, now that Denise had come so blatantly into the open, Fiona felt quite calm. It had been the undercurrents that had affected her nerves; this direct attack she could deal with.

'I'm quite sure you would do your best,' she said calmly. 'I know you're fond of him, even if it's because he resembles Logan so much. But he's not a miniature of his father, you know.'

Then Denise made her greatest mistake, made it furthermore without any idea of what she was doing from the depths of her own ignorance. 'If you mean his music,' she said scornfully, 'I can cope with that. It's an excellent party trick, but Logan wants a son to carry on here at Whangatapu, and that's what Jonathan will do.' She shrugged. 'I'm quite as ruthless as Logan, but in this case it's not for myself. Logan loves the boy, and because he wants an heir I'm happy for it to be Jonathan, even though he's your son.'

Why, Fiona thought, astounded, she doesn't know Logan at all! All she can see is the master of Whangatapu, not the man, not Logan who would never think of constraining Jonathan to a life he was not suited for.

Logan's love for his son was not a possessive emotion; he did not see his son as an extension of himself. As a Sutherland, yes, but his own person, just as he had given Fiona the freedom to call her body and emotions her own. Blinded by the Sutherland heritage and their pride in their name, Denise did not understand the man she thought she loved.

Aloud she said quietly, 'Denise, there's no necessity to go on with this conversation. It can only end in hurting you. I'm not leaving Whangatapu, and if you think you'll see why. Please don't make me spell it out to you.'

Denise laughed mirthlessly. 'Oh, I know you wouldn't go without a fight. You find life too comfortable in spite of the fact that you're only here on sufferance! Look, Fiona, make it easy for yourself. I don't like bandying insults any more than you do, but I'm prepared to be ruthless if you won't see sense. Materially you'll be well off—Logan will make sure of that! I know it will be a wrench leaving Jonathan, but surely you want the best for him? A happy home situation—you can't say you can give him that! It's common knowledge that you and Logan don't have a normal relationship—even before he told me, I knew that! There's no love between you. And even if you did manage to seduce him, I would always be around.' She hesitated, then struck home.

'You know that Logan and I are lovers, don't you? And it was his unhappiness and frustration over this farcical marriage which finally broke down his resistance when we were in Auckland. He loves me, Fiona, and I love him. Oh, he tried to be loyal, but human flesh and blood can stand so much, and what was there to be loyal to? A wife who only sees him as the father of her child, who refuses him everything, a wife who accepts all the material things he can give, yet is as cold as ice, giving nothing. There's nothing you can give Logan that I can't give him, and with it all I love him, and will go on loving him. I've proved that conclusively, by becoming his mistress.'

Fiona stood up, those pale eyes almost transparent in the pallor of her face, her mouth a bruised red. 'Denise, stop it!' she said harshly. 'If you do love Logan, I'm deeply sorry for you, but I'm not going.'

Breathing heavily, Denise said between clenched teeth, 'You—you bitch! Don't try to appeal to my better instincts, because where Logan is concerned I have none! Have you no pride at all? To stay here, knowing that your husband wants another woman—makes love to her whenever there's an opportunity.' The dark eyes blazed. 'And there'll be plenty of opportunities when I stay here! How will that affect you? To know that your husband is——'

'Denise, stop it! You can say what you like about me, or yourself, but you must not calumniate Logan like that!' Fiona took a deep breath, drawing on all her reserves of strength, praying for the right words to stop this appalling exhibition.

'Look, I'm sorry, but it won't do, you know. I neither know nor care what happened in Auckland, but if you think Logan would allow himself to indulge in a sordid intrigue in his own home under the eyes of those he loves best, then you know nothing about him. Nothing at all! Now, please, let's have an end to this. I don't think I can bear much more of it. I am *not* leaving.' She could not bring herself to tell this spoilt self-centred girl that Logan had made that impossible. Let her keep what shreds of pride remained, at least.

But Denise could not accept this. All beauty gone from her face, she advanced across the room, head thrust forward, eyes narrowed in a vicious mockery of a smile.

'Oh, but you are,' she hissed. 'Because if you don't leave here, when I tell you to go I'll make sure that everyone in the district knows just when you were married!' She stood back watching to see Fiona's reaction. 'You didn't know that I knew, did you? I was suspicious right from the start, so I got someone to check the records. If you stay here you brand your son as a bastard and yourself as a whore! *Then* see what Logan's attitude to you is. He's got more than his share of the Sutherland pride, and it will hurt him where he's most vulnerable to have it dragged in the dust. And it will kill his mother!'

'You would do that to them?'

Denise laughed, 'Gladly. I told you I was ruthless. If I can't be his wife I'll make damned sure that you get no pleasure out of taking my rightful place.'

With a swift movement Fiona stood up, suddenly angry, seeing the girl as wilfully determined to satisfy her own needs and desires no matter what the expense to others. When Fiona was angry her eyes darkened, her whole beauty became enriched and vitalised. And now she was very angry, fighting for her husband and her son, for Ailsa and Jinny.

With a chilling hauteur she said crisply, 'If nothing else had, what you've just said has convinced me that the worst thing I could do would be to leave. I'm afraid it's no use, Denise. You've overplayed your hand, to use another cliché. You've revealed that you don't understand Logan in the least, that you see everything from the viewpoint of your own selfish obsessions. As for the other—it will create a little flurry of gossip, I have no doubt, give a few spiteful tongues pleasure, but they'll get just as much pleasure from discussing your part in spreading the story, attributing motives to you. The woman scorned is yet another cliché, Denise, but it's one that's very hard to live down.'

Denise stared at her, baffled frustration evident in her stance, the fury in her expression becoming gradually supplanted by bewilderment. This was a Fiona she did not know; worse, had never realised existed. Totally in control of herself and the situation when she should have been cringing and apologetic, Fiona was showing a strength that Denise could not match.

Bitterly she said, 'You need not try to persuade me. I'll make sure that no decent person ever sets foot inside this house again, and it will be your fault!'

'Don't be stupid. You know perfectly well that that's an empty threat. This is the twentieth century, Denise, not the middle of the nineteenth, and if you go ahead with your threat people will assume that you have good reason to be so malicious. And that wouldn't please your parents.'

Defeat pinched Denise's features, drained her of colour and that vitality which was so much a part of her appeal. She felt as though she was battering against a rock, as though all of the tenets she had built her life on had suddenly proved completely without foundation. Instead of the nonentity she had believed Fiona to be she had found a woman who stood firm under blackmail and threats, who was infinitely stronger than she; at that moment of bitter defeat Denise began the slow, painful climb to adulthood, but when she looked up and saw compassion in Fiona's eyes her rancour could not be restrained.

'Don't *pity* me,' she almost snarled. 'I pity you. You'll have to live with the knowledge that you're only second best! And this will make no difference to my relationship with Logan. He does love me. He does!'

Even to her own ears it sounded more like a child's appeal for reassurance than a triumphant assertion. Fiona, now that the worst was over, felt nothing but a profound pity for her, so absorbed in herself, and up until now so assured that the crumbling of all of her assumptions must be a cruel disillusionment. Like a child who had been indulged by foolish parents, she thought that she only needed to want, and whatever she wanted would be given to her, and now that she had been brought face to face with reality she could only spit poison hopelessly.

Gently, Fiona said, 'Even if he does, there's no future in it for you, Denise. You have a lot to offer the right man. Be adult enough to accept what can't be altered.'

'Yes, you'd like to see me go, wouldn't you!' With a half sob Denise turned away, conceding the hopelessness of her position, slim shoulders bowed. 'I don't understand you,' she went on dully, 'I just don't understand you. I thought I did.'

Picking her words with great care, Fiona answered, 'You've led a very sheltered life, surrounded by people who love and admire you. My life hasn't been like that, Denise, at least, not the latter part of it. How could you expect to understand me?' She gave a twisted smile. 'I don't even understand myself, sometimes.'

Denise looked at her, really looked at her for the first time, seeing the square chin, the generous, passionate curve of the lips, the clear, calm serene eyes. On a deep breath she said slowly, 'I've been a fool, haven't I? I thought I knew so much. No—don't say anything.' She summoned a wavering smile. 'I hate you at the moment. Perhaps—after a while—I might l-learn to like you. I don't know. I think I'll go home now.'

'You'd better stay for a while,' Fiona suggested, admiring her for her courage, worried in case she was too upset to drive carefully.

'I don't think I could. Don't worry, the car knows its own way home. But before I go ... I lied to you before. Logan has never made love to me. I thought ... I thought it was because he was too honourable. I deliberately tried to give you the impression that we'd become lovers. He ... he knew what I was doing, I think. I decided last night that I would get rid of you today because ... because on the way home he told me that ... that there was nothing doing. Polite but definite; only I thought that if you left him he would turn to me.' She pressed quivering lips together, ignoring Fiona's murmur of consternation. 'I'm not stupid. I know when I'm beaten. I hope—I hope you'll be happy together,' she finished grittily, like a child forced to apologise to another against its will.

'Denise——'

'No, *don't*. Leave me some dignity! I would have taken Logan from you with the greatest of pleasure and no compunction, but I can see now that he was never mine to take. I thought I could manipulate you all, and all I've done is make a complete and utter fool of myself. Will you tell Logan?'

'No,' Fiona said quietly.

Denise shrugged. 'It doesn't matter. Nothing matters now. Oh, I shan't do anything stupid,' as she caught Fiona's worried glance. 'I'm too greedy to do that. I won't be coming to stay, of course. Tell—tell Ailsa that I've decided to go abroad with my parents—no, I'll tell her myself. I'll ring her tomorrow.' She had been walking towards the door as she spoke moving with stiff back and her head held high. Now she turned, and said, 'You're in love with him, aren't you?'

Fiona nodded.

'Yes. It explains a lot. I don't think you deserve him, but I suppose you know what you're doing. Goodbye.'

A few minutes later the car drove sedately off up the road, and Fiona found herself expelling a deep breath, the flower she had been fingering crushed to a pulpy mass in her fingers. She stared at it, then with an abrupt gesture threw it into the fireplace and went out without a backward glance.

CHAPTER ELEVEN

THE clouds had won their battle with the sun, and as evening came on a chill little wind prowled over the hills to the south, sending the casuarinas whispering together around the scented garden. Logan looked perturbed; the sheep for tomorrow's shearing were already waiting in the yards, but if it rained they would be too wet to shear, and a day would be lost while they dried out.

After dinner he went off to the shearing quarters to discuss things with the gang boss. Fiona put Jonathan to bed and met Ailsa halfway down the stairs.

'I'm going to bed,' her mother-in-law said. 'Late nights are too much for me now, and I must be fit tomorrow. I want to polish off my murderer and get the whole thing out of my system. Say goodnight to Logan for me, Fiona. Goodnight.'

It had grown cool after the warm day. Fiona set a match to the fire, pulled the curtains across and put a record on the stereo. In spite of the fact that she had had almost her full quota of sleep the night before she too felt tired. Too much emotion, she supposed, and lay quietly on the big sofa, waiting for Beethoven's Pastoral Symphony to bring her its usual healing peace.

It was not to be. Somehow, the music could not resolve the discord that raged inside her mind, making her too jittery to stay still, so that halfway through it she was pacing up and down the big, luxurious room like a caged tiger. At times like this she wished she smoked, or tatted; even the piano held no hope of resolving her indecision. It would have to be faced, and faced squarely, or she would find it hard to gain a moment's peace of mind again.

So she sat down, and tried to marshall her thoughts so that she could decide just what she should do now in the light of Denise's revelations this afternoon. She supposed that she should be pleased because her suspicions of Logan had been totally unfounded, but somehow pleasure seemed far away. Instead she was left with bitter regrets for having allowed herself to be so easily duped, remorse at her stupidity. Love had not been enough to prevent her from hurting him; she realised now that his anger had been an expression of hurt. And his pride, his arrogance, call it what you would, had prevented him from telling her the truth. Perhaps he thought she would not believe him.

'Fool!' she said half under her breath. 'Fool, fool!' Her clenched fist thumped against the arm of a chair, making her wince with pain her mind did not recognise. He had spoken of trust, and she had denied him her trust even when she professed to love him. That was where she had gone wrong, right from the start, refusing to allow him any place in her life but that of father to Jonathan. She had convinced herself that it would be an insult for him to become her husband in fact, when there was no love between them, but it had been pride on her part and—yes, she admitted it—a long-suppressed desire to pay him back for the savage disillusionment he had meted out to her five years ago. That raw patch no longer existed.

If she took Logan it would be on his terms, but the acceptance of them would be her decision. He did not want the unwilling response of her body; he had made that plain. What he wanted was more, her trust, and her faith in him. Well, that she could give. Perhaps that was all that he would accept, and yet had he not shown love of a kind in his forbearance, in his refusal to take advantage of her physical response to him?

She remembered sadly her own smugness when speaking to Stephen, not twenty-four hours before.

'Do you want Mary to prove her love?' she had asked. 'How?'

She was asking for the same thing, of course. Proof of a love that perhaps Logan could not feel. Could she accept a second-best emotion, based on the need to give Jonathan a secure and happy home? There would be mutual respect, perhaps affection, certainly passion in such a relationship. Could she *bear* it?

At last, weary but strangely triumphant, she got up and walked across to the portrait Thurston had painted of her. The painted eyes looked wistfully back a her.

Admit it, she said to the painted Fiona scornfully. You would take the man on any terms, and you'll be happy with him! Did it matter if the only times his heart beat faster for her was when they made love? He had shown, right from the start, that he was prepared to work towards making their marriage a viable thing, and she had blocked him at every turn, refusing to commit herself because of a romantic dream.

Sighing, she admitted that there would be a kind of sweetness in the less ecstatic relationship which was more than she had hoped for at the beginning. Perhaps love was best shown in the ordinary fabric of everyday life, in tolerance and laughter and the small things like whether it rained in the night before shearing started, and Jonathan's latest trick. Perhaps romance was a young girl's dream, never attained, eventually grown out of and left behind.

She walked across to the window and twitched the curtains back. The sky had cleared, although the air was still crisp. There was no moon, but Venus hung, a glittering diamond above the feathery fronds of the jacaranda tree. It was very quiet, for the stereo had switched itself off. So quiet that Logan's footsteps along the hall seemed like thunder as he walked past the door and down to the study.

Fiona turned, stared down at her hands, then swiftly turned the stereo off at the wall and went through the door. Without giving herself time to think she set off down towards the golden sliver of light which came from the half-open door of the study.

He was sorting papers, his hands dark against the whiteness, working with the swift economy of movement which was one of his characteristics. When Fiona appeared at the doorway he lifted his head, favouring her with a cool, measuring glance.

'I thought that you would be in bed by now,' he commented. 'Did you want to see me about something?'

'I—yes.' Flushing, she had to swallow before she could speak. 'I want—if you still want to, I'd like our marriage to become a real marriage.'

The papers rustled as he continued sorting them. Fiona wondered rather desperately if he had heard her, then he looked across at her, and she was horrified to see nothing but cold contempt in his eyes.

'Would you?' He sounded dangerous, more icily angry than she had ever known him.

'Yes,' she whispered, refusing to be daunted.

Another silence, shorter this time, during which her nerves tightened unbearably, then he said in tones totally devoid of expression, 'Very well. You look tired, so you go on up. I'll join you when I've finished this.'

He spoke as though they were clinching a business deal. Fiona swallowed again, before she turned and made her way out of the room. She had not expected wild transports of joy, but she had at least hoped to be met halfway. His coldness nearly made her turn tail and run from the house to hide herself in some dark place where he could never hurt her again. It was perhaps understandable that he should see her action as merely a matter of unfinished business now being brought to a conclusion, but he might at least make it seem a satisfactory conclusion, she thought bitterly. He *must* know how much effort those few words had taken, what was implicit in her capitulation! Why was he so angry with her?

She stopped on the stairs, one hand clenched on the satin-smooth coolness of the wooden banister, then deliberately relaxed it and continued climbing. There could be no going back now. If he was angry it was probably because he thought of the time wasted, and that was her fault. All of the times he had wooed her with the turbulent sweetness of his kisses came back, each one clear as a print, to her mind. If she had surrendered to her own emotions and his needs on any one of those occasions there would have been no humiliation in her surrender, so that it was her stubbornness which had led to this situation. That arrogant control of his had been tried too often and she had to pay the price or live in the limbo which had be their marriage until now.

The door of the bedroom was half open. Fiona pushed it to behind her, snapped on the light and stood for a moment, surveying it. So much luxury, and yet there had been little happiness for her in it. Here she had cried for the moon, only to have it denied her. But she could give Logan her love, freely and without counting the cost, and perhaps that would sweeten the bitter knowledge that it would be Venus, goddess of passion, who reigned in this room.

So, like a bride on her wedding night, she prepared herself for him, showering, brushing her hair into a cloak of red about her shoulders. The nightgown she chose was of silk, a long, severely Grecian style, the colour of her hair but many shades lighter. Through the transparent fabric her skin gleamed whitely like the marble of a statue.

When she was ready, she turned off the light and drifted across to the window, unable to make the final commitment of getting into the big bed. The stars blazed like jewels in a black velvet sky, and over all was the pale light of the evening star, that elusive shadowy radiance in which Logan had kissed her under the jasmine. The jasmine was almost over now, but she thought she could still detect a hint of the heavy scent on the air.

Somewhere a morepork, the little hunter of the night, gave his mournful cry 'More-pork, more-pork' warning all small denizens of tree and grass that the night was good for hunting. Fiona had once seen one mobbed by a flock of starlings in the bright light of day. It had looked comical, a tiny owl which stared at its tormentors in bewilderment before launching itself into the darkness and safety of the deep bush. That was how she felt now, bewildered, frightened, longing for a refuge, yet through all these emotions ran a thread of anticipation which could not be denied, and when she shivered it was not from the cold.

The soft thud of the door into Logan's room sounded like a knell on her ear; she tensed, knuckles white in her fingers as she heard him moving about. The shower hissed, then there were long minutes of waiting before the door opened and he came in.

By now her eyes were thoroughly accustomed to the darkness so that she could see him without difficulty. In the dimness he looked huge, a forbidding figure against the pale door, a dark bathrobe wrapped around him. Almost immediately he switched the lights on so that she had to blink several times before her vision cleared.

There was insolent appraisal in the look he gave her, but his face was set and unsmiling. Flushing, she felt her whole body go hot as his glance raked it, but she forced herself to meet his merciless eyes when they lifted to her face.

'Come here,' he said softly.

Holding his gaze with her own, she walked across the room, for miles it seemed, in the bright light. He loomed ahead, big and tough and cruel, yet her heart thumped crazily in her breast, so loud that she felt sure he could hear it.

'Well?' he mocked, when she stopped only inches away from him. He had not moved a muscle since the light had gone on, but stood still with his arms folded across his chest, leaning back against the door.

It was torture of an exquisitely refined type. Fiona bit her lip, then reached up and slid her hands around his neck and offered him herself to do with as he wished. Her surrender was as complete and absolute as he could have wished, but he still did not move, though flames warmed the cold depths of his eyes, searing her pleading face with their intensity.

'Why the change, Fiona?' he demanded, through lips that scarcely moved.

She shook her head, whispering, 'Does it matter?' Even at this late stage she wished to hold on to the remnants of her pride.

'Yes. I want to know what brought about this sudden change of heart.' His glance narrowed, became cruel. 'Have you decided to light fire with fire, take a leaf out of Denise's book and try a bit of seduction?'

She was angry now, but when she went to pull away his hands moved swiftly, pinioning her wrists so that she was forced to stay where she was. Drawing a quivering breath which hurt her lungs, she said, 'And if I have? What then?'

'It will be interesting to see if you have the courage to go through with it,' he returned before his mouth covered hers in a kiss that was totally lacking in tenderness or respect.

For a moment she panicked, trying to fight herself out of his arms, but they were a cruel imprisonment subduing her effortlessly, and soon she was unable to think, lost in the dark power of his passion, responding as she had never been able to before to his expert lovemaking. In some dim, faraway recess of her mind she knew that this was not making love, this was seduction, but his mouth and hands kindled a fire within her that could only be assuaged by complete union with him, and when he picked her up and carried her across to the bed she did not protest.

He laid her on the bed, slipped off his robe and came in beside her, his body hard against her, his mouth sensuous against her skin, his hands carelessly experienced as they removed her nightdress. She shivered, meeting the devouring fire of his glance, but stroked the warm damp skin of his shoulders, pressing kisses to the brown column of his throat, and then a dark tide of ecstasy carried her away to a complete mindlessness in which a voice she did not recognise gasped his name.

Sated, they slept in each other's arms, but it was still dark when Fiona woke, although one of the farm cockerels crowed triumphantly, so dawn was not far off. Slowly, moving her stiff body carefully so that she wouldn't wake him, she got up, went into the bathroom and ran herself a glass of water.

The liquid ran cold and sweet down her dry throat, but there was a hot ache behind her eyes that could not be so easily assuaged, and for several moments she leaned, slumped against the cool tiles of the wall. Life had never, even in her blackest moments, seemed so futile, so devoid of every hope and comfort. Was it always to be like this? Passion, then satiation, then the bitter aftermath of frustrated love. In time, no doubt, she would become accustomed to the fact that Logan possessed every quality one could hope for in a lover except tenderness, but at the moment it seemed the worst humiliation she had ever suffered to hope that her sensitivities would become so dulled that it no longer hurt.

The little core of unquenchable courage that was hers to call upon when life threw its worst at her came to her aid now. Straightening up, she went back into the room she had, of her own volition, made the source of her unhappiness. Logan stirred as she slipped between the sheets, then said thickly, 'You could have brought one for me.'

'I didn't know you were awake,' she said. 'Shall I get you one?'

'Please.'

He switched the light on, watching her beneath half-closed lids as she walked across the room, performing this menial task. Well, she thought bitterly, she had chosen this role herself. Logan's wife, to run around after him as he wished. God send her strength to be able to do it uncomplainingly, a service to her love for him.

He drank the water thirstily, then waited as she once more climbed into the bed.

'Aren't you going to put the light out?' she asked carefully, afraid to move too closely to him lest he construe it as an invitation to more of his soulless lovemaking. She had thought—ages ago, it seemed—that once she had surrendered her body to him her troubles would be over, or almost all of them. Odd how life kicked you in the teeth, for they were only just beginning!

'No. We have to talk,' he returned with uncompromising directness.

Surprised, Fiona turned to look at him, became caught up in the physical presence of him, the way his hair grew across his brow, the dark, unfairly long lashes, the short stubble on his chin and cheeks; like her, the tension had not entirely gone from his expression, but he was more relaxed than she had ever seen him before.

Her heart contracted unbearably. At least she had given him that, physical ease.

'No, discussion first,' he said teasingly, and smiled at the blush his words brought to her cheeks. 'After last night I didn't think you would ever blush for me again,' he ended meaningly.

'Don't—you're unfair,' she said, confusion lowering her lashes. 'What is there to discuss?'

'As if you didn't know.'

Could that be tenderness in his voice? Fiona didn't know, but her breath came quickly to her throat as he touched the dark mark on her shoulder. 'You look very morning after the night beforeish, which I thoroughly approve of. Where did you get that bruise?'

Fugitive mischief sparkled in her eyes, but her voice was demure as she replied, 'You don't know your own strength.'

He covered the discoloured spot with his mouth, drawing the pain and tenderness from it, then said lazily, 'I didn't care overmuch last night, but I'm sorry I was rough with you. Still, when a dam bursts someone is usually hurt, and last night was a fairly cataclysmic affair. Now, stop seducing me from the path of duty. You and I have some clearing up to do. I still want to know why you decided to allow me my legal rights to your person last night. I'm damned sure you had no such intention yesterday morning.'

'No,' Fiona said slowly. She hesitated, then without any further holding back, committed herself fully to him and to the life and position he had given her. Only complete honesty would serve now, and to hell with her pride.

'It was the culmination of several things,' she said, trying to take no notice of the way he was playing with a lock of her hair, winding it round his finger as though he loved the feel of it. 'I knew I couldn't hold out against you much longer, for obvious reasons, but while I thought you were in love with Denise I wouldn't be used as a—well, as a kind of substitute.'

'You thought I was in *love* with Denise?' He sounded incredulous. 'I thought I'd made it quite clear that although I may have had ideas of marrying her, I was never in love with her.'

'You made nothing clear,' she retorted with some asperity. 'How on earth was I expected to know what you felt? I didn't know you at all, had no idea how you thought or reacted, and she made it more than clear that she felt she had some claims on you. At first I thought it was only that you had decided that she was the most suitable wife for you, but——' she hesitated, pleating the sheet between nervous fingers, not daring to look at him.

'But——' he prompted, giving nothing away.

'Well, things were strained, and when she came back from Auckland she—well, you know. You saw her, and you knew very well what her whole attitude implied.'

'I know what you inferred from it,' he said tersely. 'I was never more angry in my life—even though I hoped that a little healthy jealousy might bring you to your senses.'

'Yes, well—in a way it did. Only I thought that if you had become her lover it was because you really loved her. I couldn't believe that you would make love to her unless it was that.'

'You knew *that* about me, at least,' he said, giving her hair a sharp tug.

'I decided to go, and leave the field clear for her. Jonathan is fond of her, and she of him. Then you told me that I wasn't to go, and you spoke to me of trust, and I realised that I hadn't trusted you at all. I'd taken everything, security, your love for Jonathan, Whangatapu—and you'd tried to make a go of it, and I'd given you nothing. So I decided that it was time I gave you something—not out of gratitude, or anything like that, but because if you loved Denise all that I could give you was myself, as a kind of—refuge, I suppose.' She lifted her lashes slowly, looked directly into the beloved face and added quietly, 'You see, I love you, Logan. I think I must always have loved you, even in the years when I thought I would never see you again. All I want is for you to be happy.'

'Liar,' he said unevenly, drawing her close to him with hands which were wonderfully gentle. 'You want more than that, so don't pretend to be so noble and self-sacrificing.'

She laughed, believing at last what his eyes and hands and voice revealed, 'You're right, of course. I'm sorry if you do love Denise, because I sent her away yesterday, and if I see her too much in the future I'll end up by scratching her eyes out!'

Helplessly he began to laugh, the sounds muffled in her hair, and she felt an inexpressible warmth flood her whole being; a revitalising, healing surge of emotions as she realised just what it was that he had not yet told her, the key that was being handed to her, the key to a happiness such as she had never expected and did not deserve.

She had not long to wait. 'Oh, Fiona, you darling idiot,' he said at last, kissing her forehead and then her eyelids, smoothing the tumbled hair with a tender hand. 'I love you so much, you silly wench, and you've led me such a dance! I should beat you unmercifully.'

'I bruise very easily,' she murmured dulcetly, holding him very tightly against her, rejoicing as she had not been able to before in their closeness. Love for him made her breathless; she wanted to tell him how much, but no words came, and she could only burrow her head into his chest and press herself fiercely against him.

'Not yet,' he said, lazily amused but with a thread of

passion in his voice which excited her unbearably.

Obedient, she relaxed her hold, but traced with delicate touch the contours of his face and throat, absorbed wholly in the wonder of being able to allow her hands and thoughts and emotions full licence.

'Logan, why did you let Denise get away with so much?' she asked gravely.

'I hoped to make you jealous.' Capturing her hand, he kissed the palm, then held it firmly. 'Let's get the explanations over, shall we, and then there'll be no more doubts. Before you came on the scene I'd more or less decided that Denise would be as suitable a wife as any I could find.'

'Cold-bloodedly?'

He nodded. 'I'm afraid so. She was in love with the idea of being a Sutherland and I was fond of her. You must admit, my darling, that she's lovely enough to stir any man's blood.'

Hearing him say that even now made her jealous. Unable to trust herself to speech, she nodded.

'Then we met again, and I wanted Jonathan. In my cold-blooded way I decided that you could be licked into shape as a wife, and married you. I'm not a patient man, but I wasn't going to rush you in any way. You had paid a very high price for one night of folly, and I couldn't press you, knowing that. What I didn't bargain for was how you affected me.' He tipped her chin so that he could see her face, and said wryly, 'I could hardly keep my hands off you, and I had to erect a few barriers of my own in case things got out of hand. Hence the bouts of bad temper. It was a hellish situation. You behaved like a shrinking violet, Jinny was intransigent, Mother dubious, Danny boiling up for trouble, and Denise doing her damnedest to throw a spanner in the works. Believe me, I nearly hauled you into bed with me just to get rid of one of my worries! In fact, I was seriously thinking of doing just that—you had shown me that you could respond in a most satisfactory way to me. Then—something happened, and left me completely winded, like a callow youth in his first love affair.'

'What?' she asked curiously.

'I realised that I loved you,' he said simply. 'Just like that. The day when you waited for us under the walnut tree, after the garden club left. You hugged Jonathan, and seeing you there, your eyes hazy with tiredness, our child in your arms, I thought—there's the only woman I've ever wanted. It wasn't just physical, as I thought, it was a need that was deeper and more fundamental than that. I couldn't handle it. I didn't know what to do. When I brought you to Whangatapu I was quite sure that you would love me within a month, but your defences were never breached, except physically. And that was no longer enough for me. I wanted all of you, but you gave me no sign of how you felt about me.'

'And you're not a patient man,' she whispered lovingly. 'You were remarkably patient with me.'

They kissed then, a long affirmation of love and tenderness, a kiss without passion, a promise and a fulfilment.

'Don't interrupt me,' he bade her sternly. 'I suppose you realise that shearing starts as soon as it gets light? We've not much time, my love. Not that there's much more to tell. I let Denise carry on the way she did because I thought a little jealousy might help you to make up your mind. So I made sure that you couldn't run away again and waited for developments. I didn't think they would be so fast coming. That kiss you saw was the only one—a thank-you for taking her to Auckland with me. She made the most of it, of course, and I didn't mind. I wanted you to be jealous, but when I saw the revulsion in your eyes I knew it was a mistake.'

Fiona laughed, but said soberly, 'Last night—why were you so cold, so—so impersonal about the whole thing?'

'I knew Denise had been; I saw her go, and had a pretty fair idea of what had happened.' He lifted himself on one elbow, looking down at her with a wry smile. 'I don't really know why I behaved like that. I didn't intend to take you until all this had been sorted out, but I lost control of the whole situation the minute you touched me, and it was too late then. And,' dropping a swift kiss on the hollow between her breasts, 'I must confess that something unregenerate and primitive in me enjoyed the taking, especially as it was quite obvious that you enjoyed it too.'

'Barbarian!' she mocked, winding her arms around his neck to pull him close.

'True.' He looked exultantly into her eyes, and laughed the low dangerous laughter of a conqueror, saying before their lips met again, 'But I'm going to enjoy this more, darling heart, because there are no barriers between us at all, now. You're my wife, and all our dealings together will be like this, with love.'

She held him off a moment longer. 'What about the shearing, darling?'

'Damn the shearing!'

And so it was as it was going to be from now on, love and laughter and passion blended together to make an ecstatic fulfilment.

Romances you have loved

Mills & Boon Best Seller Romances are the love stories that have proved particularly popular with our readers. They really are "back by popular demand." These are the other titles to look out for this month.

THE DARK SIDE OF MARRIAGE
by Margery Hilton

It was two years since the marriage of Nick and Karen Radcliffe had ended in disaster — but Nick's beloved adoptive mother didn't know that, and now that she was dying and wanted them near her, he was determined that she should not find out. And so Karen found herself forced once again to live with this man who had nothing but contempt for her — and trying desperately to control the longing she still felt for him . . .

FORBIDDEN LOVE
by Rachel Lindsay

Venetia was not looking forward to working in Hong Kong as secretary to a neurotic, unhappily married woman. The job turned out to be even more problem-filled than she had feared — and the biggest problem of all was her employer's attractive husband . . .

ROOTED IN DISHONOUR
by Anne Mather

Beth was genuinely fond of Willard Petrie, which was why she had agreed to marry him and go to live in his Caribbean island home. But 'genuinely fond' was hardly the way to describe how she had begun to feel about Raoul Valerian. Could she fight the feeling and remain loyal to Willard?

Mills & Boon

the rose of romance